Advance acclaim for *The Rebirth of Cold Fusion*

"*The Rebirth of Cold Fusion* is a very important and timely book. It may help educate a generation of physicists told to believe cold fusion doesn't exist. I look forward to future editions describing a definitive theory of the phenomenon."

> - Robert H. Parmenter, Emeritus Professor of Physics, University of Arizona, and co-author of "Cold Fusion in Metals" (Proceedings, National Academy of Science, Vol. 86, 1989) with Willis E. Lamb, Nobel prize winner in Physics, 1955

"Basic research and its progress depend upon how open the society is to accept new ideas and pursue them to the end - right or wrong. *The Rebirth of Cold Fusion* brings out the important question of whether the present form of peer review and financial control by government agencies help in new innovations or not. It is obvious that some changes have to be made, with the future in view."

> - Dr. P. K. Iyengar, Chairman (retired), Atomic Energy Commission, India

"The Rebirth of Cold Fusion is an important report in the good tradition of American investigative journalism. It exposes a scandalous case of scientific misconduct, engages those who are guilty of foul play, and sets the record straight. The book comes at a critical moment in which a neglected field of inquiry is fighting for recognition. Let's hope it helps cold fusion gain the support a potential energy source deserves. Everybody should be aware of the facts in this book."

> - Haiko Lietz, Science Reporter, Germany

D1590649

About Cold Fusion

"The only thing pathological about cold fusion is the way the scientific establishment has treated it."

- Sharon Begley, "Cold Fusion Isn't Dead, It's Just Withering From Scientific Neglect" (Wall Street Journal), Sep. 5, 2003

"No cover-up like this has happened before. It is a profound scandal in American science."

- Charles Beaudette, author, *Excess Heat & Why Cold Fusion Research Prevailed*, 2002

"In regard to cold fusion, it would be advisable for the scientific community to brace itself for the fallout that will be coming soon when the public starts to become aware that the scientific community was engaging in an act of gross self-deception back in 1989."

- Brian Josephson, Nobel prize for physics, 1973

"Cold fusion may provide a clean nuclear energy to mankind. Since I have worked long in nuclear engineering, it is a dream of nuclear energy."

- Akito Takahashi, professor, department of nuclear engineering, graduate school of engineering, Osaka University

"If Professor X.Z. Li [Tsinghua University, China] is correct, then I'll have to throw away about 14 of the 16 chapters in my book *Introduction to Fusion Energy*, because it will no longer be relevant to the kinds of fusion that could result from this 'cold fusion' process."

- Dr. J. Reece Roth, head of the industrial plasma engineering group, University of Tennessee

The Rebirth
Of
Cold Fusion

Real Science, Real Hope, Real Energy

Steven B. Krivit and Nadine Winocur, Psy.D.

Foreword by Sir Arthur C. Clarke

Pacific Oaks Press
Los Angeles, CA, USA

Published by
Pacific Oaks Press
Los Angeles, California, 90064

Library of Congress Control Number: 2004097142

ISBN 0-9760545-8-2

Current Affairs / General Science

Cover Design: Craig Erlick
Printed in the United States of America
October 2004

This book is dedicated to the memory of

Steven's father,

Lawrence Robert Krivit, M.D.

Healer, Inventor, Visionary

Massachusetts Institute of Technology graduate, 1952
Medical College of Virginia graduate, 1958

And to the memory of

Eugene Mallove, Sc.D.
Champion of Cold Fusion Research Worldwide
Founder of *Infinite Energy* magazine and the New Energy Foundation

Massachusetts Institute of Technology graduate, 1970
Harvard doctoral graduate, 1975

"There are those that look at things the way they are, and ask why?
I dream of things that never were, and ask why not. "

- Robert F. Kennedy

Contents

PART THREE: DISCOVERIES AND MYSTERIES

PART FOUR: REFLECTION AND ANTICIPATION

Acknowledgments

It has been an honor and a pleasure to make the acquaintance of so many people of immeasurable character and heart. Since March 23, 1989 onward, you have pursued scientific truths, propelled by your inner wisdom and humbled by the possibilities of the unknown. We salute you! And we thank you not only for showing us secrets of nature unrevealed to ordinary scientists but also for demonstrating conviction in your beliefs.

This project stands on the shoulders of several great people. We recognize and thank Gene Mallove, who, in his 1991 book *Fire From Ice: Searching for the Truth Behind the Cold Fusion Furor*, courageously expressed the truth that cold fusion is real, long before any science journalist dared to ask questions that challenged the prevailing view. Gene maintained the torch that initially drew us to his research facility and that lit our own passion to investigate the brewing mystery of cold fusion. Without Gene's tenacity and vigor, we suspect that this field may have lost the required energy to carry it through its dark years in the early 1990s. Your spirit and accomplishments live on, Gene.

We also thank George Miley, who, as the former editor of *Fusion Technology*, modeled integrity in science journalism and stuck his neck out where few others would dare, by publishing studies of sound scientific merit that others rejected for political reasons.

Our project would not have been possible without the work of Charles Beaudette, who dedicated six years to chronicling the travails and science of cold fusion in his book *Excess Heat & Why Cold Fusion Prevailed*. For the brilliant road map you provided and for your assistance in clarifying key concepts, Charles, we thank you.

Words cannot express our gratitude to and appreciation for Ed Storms, who provided sage advice and steadfast guidance, which at times during the 12-month production of this book included daily phone support. Ed taught us about cold fusion research, from the broad to the specific. He clarified our misperceptions, and he gently and repeatedly steered us back when we were off the mark. Ed, for us and many others, your teachings have been a lighthouse in a stormy sea; you will be remembered and appreciated for a long, long time.

We are truly grateful for Dave Nagel, a pioneer who has worked tirelessly to develop a path for cold fusion to gain acceptance as a legitimate science. As we go to press, we do not know the direction of the Department of Energy's current assessment of cold fusion, but if good news arrives, we suspect that Dave, and a few helpers, deserve much credit for the sheer work involved in bringing this about.

Before the Department of Energy review, Dave played a direct role in this project by providing us information, advice and direction for the predecessor to this book, "The 2004 Cold Fusion Report." Scott Chubb also played a key role by providing extensive information of which, unfortunately, because of its highly technical nature, we were able to include only a fraction in this book. Dave and Scott, we thank you for your belief in us, for your enthusiasm for this project and for your generosity.

We also thank Jed Rothwell, who, together with Ed Storms, for the last few years has thanklessly provided an immense public service by digitizing and publishing hundreds of cold fusion papers on the www.lenr-canr.org library. Because of the neglect by the established journals, cold fusion evidence surely would have remained in the dark for many ages without the lenr-canr.org library.

Earlier in our research, we consulted two skeptical plasma physicists, one at Lawrence Livermore and one at an atomic energy company in San Diego, who requested anonymity. They perhaps offered the most important sounding board for this project, confirming for us that the information we had obtained from the cold fusion community made sense and offered value to the larger scientific community. It was a pleasure speaking with you gentlemen and discussing the strengths and weaknesses of our investigative findings. We hope that this work will re-ignite hope for your own dreams of viable fusion power.

Lest we forget, our dutiful and devoted editors, Cindy Goldstein and Diane Winocur, despite their full lives and schedules, graciously found every flaw (we hope) and provided expert guidance on many aspects of the presentation of our work. Cindy, you came through for us at the right time, on time. You are to be commended for putting up with our chaos.

We are also and especially grateful for our technical reviewers. Thank you for trudging through the very rough drafts of our work to ensure the book's technical and historical accuracy. This was truly a team effort. Without the confidence (and corrections) gained by your review, it would not have been possible. Any remaining errors are, of course, our responsibility alone.

We thank Vince Golubic, who provided an immense wealth of knowledge pertaining to general as well as nuclear science. Vince was of tremendous assistance with many sections of Part One and with the introduction to this book. We can truly say that, when we set out to include the broader subjects in Part One, we could not have achieved this result without your knowledge, creativity, and thoughtful contributions.

Thanks also go to Haiko Lietz who provided a critical eye to our earlier work and kindly identified its strengths and weaknesses, helping to make this book what it is.

Craig Erlick is a masterful graphic artist who, within minutes of discussion, understood what we wished to express on the cover and delivered a stunning job that far exceeded our expectations. You were a pleasure to work with, Craig.

We are most grateful to Elizabeth Safran who, in the middle of her very hectic schedule, provided public relations assistance essential to the success of this project.

We also wish to acknowledge the assistance of reference librarian Randy Souther who, without hesitation, assisted us in obtaining many important materials.

To our family and friends, who initially bit their tongues when we talked about our "cold fusion" project, and whose polite tolerance (because of their disbelief) evolved into genuine interest, enthusiasm, encouragement and assistance, we are extremely grateful. We will spend time with you soon. Promise.

Several friends, relatives and authors assisted at various times with their inspiration, ideas and moral support. Among these we especially wish to thank Holmes Fetherolf, Jeane Manning, Howard Bronson, Christina Smith, Scott Grusky and Barry Leneman.

Steve wishes to extend a special "thank you" to Nadine. Thank you for your patience, your care, and your precision. I know this hasn't been easy. Thank you for hanging in there and for the choices you made to contribute to this project and to the greater good.

Foreword

by Sir Arthur C. Clarke

In March 1989, two respected chemists, Drs. Martin Fleischmann and Stanley Pons, hit the headlines in a way that few scientists do in an entire career.

They claimed to have achieved nuclear fusion at room temperature in certain metals saturated with deuterium, the heavy isotope of hydrogen. Under these conditions, they reported, they were generating more energy than they had put into the system.

This claim caused a global sensation, and many laboratories tried to repeat the experiment. Almost all reported failure, and Pons and Fleischmann became known as charlatans. That was the last that anyone heard of them – for several years.

From the mid-1990s, however, an underground movement of scientists decided that these claims should be investigated more seriously. They developed experiments of their own, often in defiance of their employers. There have been several international conferences on so-called "cold fusion" which have been derided by sceptics as congregations of deluded disciples worshipping a false religion.

Some of the scepticism appeared valid: If Drs. Pons and Fleischmann had indeed produced nuclear fusion, they should have been dead! For where are the neutrons and gamma rays, the lethal emissions such a reaction should produce? Where are the nuclear "ashes" of tritium and helium? Well, later experiments confirmed the presence of tritium, which can result only from a nuclear reaction, though in quantities far too small to account for the energy liberated. However, numerous experiments also demonstrated findings of helium-4 in amounts which do account for the energy liberated. This is a monumental achievement in the understanding of cold fusion.

Clearly, the mysteries are dissolving, and understanding is coming into view. Recently, plausible theories have been proposed which explain the absence of radiation, through energy transfer to the microscopic surfaces of the palladium in the form of heat. A fully predictive theoretical basis for cold fusion remains a mystery, as was the energy produced by radioactivity and uranium fission, when they were first discovered.

The neglect of cold fusion is one of the biggest scandals in the history of science. As I wrote in *Profiles of the Future* (1962), "With monotonous regularity, apparently competent men have laid down the law about what is technically possible or impossible – and have been proved utterly wrong, sometimes while the ink was scarcely dry from their pens. On careful analysis, it appears that these debacles fall into two classes, which I will call Failures of Nerve and Failures of Imagination."

In 1989, the cold fusion controversy fitted into the second category, Failures of Imagination, which comes into play when all the available facts are appreciated and marshaled correctly but when the really vital facts are still undiscovered and the possibility of their existence is not even admitted.

Today, the cold fusion controversy falls into the first category, Failures of Nerve; many vital facts have been discovered, yet sceptics lack the courage to acknowledge them or their immense implications.

The Rebirth of Cold Fusion, by Steven B. Krivit and Nadine Winocur, takes a fresh look at this still unresolved debate. An unbiased reader finishing this book will sense that something strange and wonderful is happening at the "fringes" of science. Although hard-core physicists remain fond of intoning "pathological science" like a mantra, I cannot quite believe that hundreds of highly credentialed scientists working at laboratories around the world can all be deluding themselves for years.

As for the sceptics, I can do no better than to quote my own First Law, which I first expressed more than 40 years ago: "When a distinguished but elderly scientist says something is possible, (s)he is almost certainly right. But when (s)he says something is impossible, (s)he is very probably wrong."

Perhaps the most disappointing outcome would be if cold fusion turns out to be merely a laboratory curiosity, of some theoretical interest but of no practical importance. But this seems unlikely; anything so novel would indicate a major breakthrough. The energy produced by the first uranium

xvi

fission experiments was trivial, but everyone with any imagination knew what it would lead to.

Of course, the most exciting possibility would be if these anomalous energy results can be scaled up. That could terminate the era of fossil fuels, end worries about pollution and climate change, and alter the geopolitical structure of our world completely out of recognition.

In 1973, when the Organization of the Petroleum Exporting Countries started to multiply oil prices, I rashly predicted, "The age of cheap power is over – the age of free power is still 50 years ahead."

This book strengthens my hope that this may not be too far from the truth.

Sir Arthur C. Clarke
Fellow, King's College, London

Colombo, Sri Lanka
14 June 2004

Introduction

The cold fusion phenomenon was introduced to the world in a press conference in Utah in 1989. This news conference created a media spectacle unlike any newly introduced science had ever seen. Since that time, the words cold fusion have taken hold in the public mind and become synonymous with claims of achieving the impossible, whether in the miraculous or in the fraudulent sense. Cold fusion has gained marketing status as a rock band, a frozen energy bar and computer software. Its popular appeal as the holy grail of energy has even become subject matter for several science fiction movies.

As a global village, we face desperate times. The world needs an alternative energy source to supply our ravenous and dramatically increasing energy consumption. Fifteen years ago, cold fusion presented an ideal solution that offered both clean energy from an abundant source and the end of environmental pollutants. More than ever before, scientists working in this field feel optimistic that this energy will be harvested one day and that the spigots of the fossil fuel age can be slowly turned off.

The science skeptics of 1989 decided that *cold* fusion was impossible. According to standard nuclear physics theory, they are right. Since the early 1950s, *hot* fusion scientists and engineers have spent $16 billion on fusion research using massive building-sized systems and standard nuclear theories. The idea that nuclear reactions could occur with a beaker of heavy water, a pinch of salt, two electrodes and a battery seemed quite inconceivable to them.

Yet some, having contemplated a more open-minded and optimistic view, have labored to reproduce the astonishing claims in their own laboratories. Fifteen years later, a body of experimental evidence from established researchers worldwide has begun to bend bookshelves. Paradoxically, at the same time, U.S. cold fusion laboratories both large and small are grossly neglected and inadequately equipped to investigate this new science more fully.

As in the early reports 15 years ago, a large body of experiments now demonstrate unexplained levels of heat which surpass the amount of energy used in the experiment. Reports continue to show low levels of tritium and verifiable amounts of helium-4, both products of a nuclear reaction. These were the first hints of a new paradigm of which today's orthodox nuclear scientists are exceedingly skeptical: the transmutation of elements in a science domain other than high-energy physics.

Having evolved, the field of cold fusion now comprises a broad variety of experiments and theories. Many of these may represent not fusion but, more precisely, low energy nuclear reactions, also known as LENR effects. Ardent experimenters have developed numerous techniques to stimulate low energy nuclear reactions, and several theories have emerged, some of which challenge the basic precepts of traditional atomic physics. Scientists and laypeople alike who study cold fusion today still pinch themselves with disbelief, and they wonder how this low energy realm could occur within nature's mysterious atomic world.

For all these reasons and more, cold fusion presents potential risks and rewards like no other energy source, past or present. Its nature and experimental findings have been grossly misinterpreted, misconstrued and maligned. This book attempts to set the record straight. Several dozen cold fusion scientists have contributed information about their research - so many that we can safely say not only that this is an accurate history and depiction of the field but also that it represents the voice of the cold fusion community. In an endeavor to educate and safely nurture the emergence of this new energy source, *The Rebirth of Cold Fusion* presents a hopeful and exciting chronicle of astounding facts and events that explore the world of cold fusion.

Preface

The Rebirth of Cold Fusion is an investigative report written to demonstrate that cold fusion is a legitimate new field of science, that its researchers deserve recognition, respect and support, and that society deserves to benefit from whatever technologies may arise from this discovery.

This book is not a complete survey of the entire field of cold fusion or related experimentation. The authors regret that practical constraints did not permit discussion of all of the hundreds of excellent scientists who have made historic contributions to science in the cold fusion field over the last 15 years. Indeed, some of those featured in this text have attained additional noteworthy achievements that are not reflected in this book.

The authors' backgrounds are in computer and behavioral sciences; they do not purport to be experts in the physical sciences. However, they have been privileged and honored to learn directly from some of the world's brightest and most innovative electrochemists, nuclear physicists, metallurgists, radiochemists, engineers and others, including a few rocket scientists.

Several prominent members of this community have reviewed this book for technical accuracy. Several scientists with decades of experience in hot fusion also have reviewed portions of this book.

The investigation behind this book arose from Steven's naive curiosity, he admits. He learned about cold fusion in 1989 from radio reports and from his local community newspaper, but not from television. At the time, he had taken a vow of abstinence from television viewing.

Oddly, while the initial news of cold fusion was carried throughout all media outlets, its apparent demise, months later, was carried almost exclusively on television and in larger newspapers. Consequently, he missed entirely the fact that cold fusion had been "disproved."

By 1999, curious as to why, after many years, he had heard no news of cold fusion, Steven began searching for answers. His investigative journey eventually brought him into contact with dozens of cold fusion scientists from around the world. Many initially were reluctant to speak with him, because they had been harmed by news stories that placed them in a less-than-favorable light. Yet they found in Steven an unbiased listener who was willing to spend the time required to understand the information and to convey the facts accurately.

Steven's investigation heightened in 2003, when scientists whom he video-interviewed at the 10th International Conference on Cold Fusion presented him with many pieces of information which, when combined with previously gathered data, formed a coherent story. This was the turning point for him, when he shifted from a curious and skeptical observer to one who understood that the scientists performing this work were credible, their methodologies scientific, and their integrity excellent. Nadine joined in at this point to help download the information in Steven's head and put it into writing.

While the authors are aware of numerous new, clean fuel technologies on the horizon, they believe that cold fusion is the best current hope for a pollution-free source of energy that will permit a sustainable future for this planet. The authors are also concerned that cold fusion might achieve capacities that may not be applied toward peaceful uses, and responsible nations worldwide are encouraged to take notice.

Part One of this book examines the current environmental and scientific context for the development of cold fusion - why it is needed and how it compares with other potential alternative energy sources. It also defines basic concepts that are discussed in the remaining sections. Part Two delves into the history of cold fusion, including many human stories and anecdotes. Part Three provides in-depth scientific evidence supporting the validity of this new science. Part Four reflects on sociopolitical issues relevant to the assimilation of a radical technology into the established geopolitical and economic structure.

Steven B. Krivit
Nadine Winocur, Psy.D.

Los Angeles, California, USA
Sept. 20, 2004

Part One

GLOBAL ENERGY,

GLOBAL CONCERNS

CHAPTER ONE

Cold Fusion Basics

In simple terms, cold fusion is a scientific phenomenon that occurs in a room-temperature experimental arrangement and produces nuclear energy, in the form of heat, without harmful radiation.

Cold fusion flies in the face of 70 years of accepted hot fusion and atomic theory that states that fusion can occur only under extreme, multimillion-degree temperatures. While cold fusion experiments show every indication of some sort of fusion or, perhaps, some other as-yet-unexplained process, the debate is not really about fusion *per se*, which is accepted. The debate, rather, is about whether fusion is possible in this new "cold" method.

Cold fusion appears embarrassingly simple when compared to hot fusion. Many nuclear physicists cannot conceive that a cell, which is no larger than an adult hand, can exhibit a single spark of nuclear energy. However, as any solid-state physicist will attest, many things can happen at the sub-atomic level inside atoms. In essence, the microscopic surface of the palladium metal, along with an as-yet-theorized determining factor, appears to provide the proper "squeeze," if you will, to allow deuterium nuclei to fuse.

Fusion's Fuel: Ocean Water

For decades, scientists in both the hot and cold fusion fields have hoped that fusion finally will solve the world's energy problems. If fusion power becomes commercially viable, it has the potential to fulfill the world's energy needs, using ocean water as fuel, safely, without greenhouse gasses or nuclear waste.

Most fusion experiments use a form of hydrogen known as deuterium for fuel. Deuterium atoms (Figure 1-1) are considered isotopes of hydrogen, because they have the same single proton that hydrogen does, but they also have one extra neutron.

In cold fusion experiments, deuterium may be used in a liquid or gaseous form. As a liquid, deuterium takes the form of D_2O, or more commonly, "heavy water," because it is 10 percent heavier than normal water. In the gas form, deuterium is noted as D_2. Cold fusion reactions also require and occur in the presence of a metal, typically palladium but sometimes titanium or nickel.

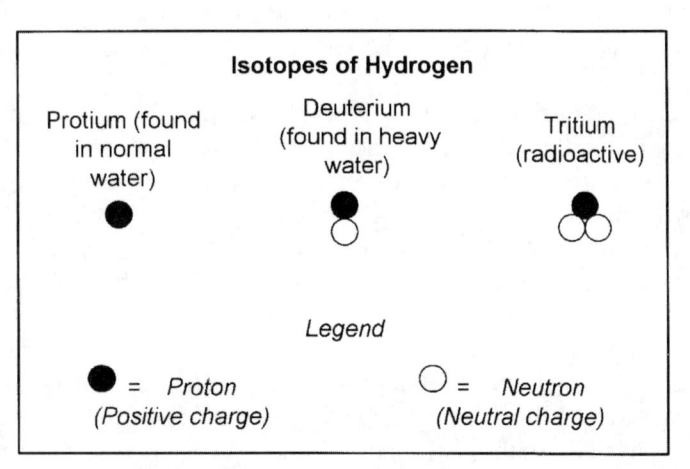

Figure 1-1. Isotopes of Hydrogen: Protium, Deuterium & Tritium

Deuterium is naturally abundant in ocean water. With the vastness of the oceans, nature may, in fact, have given humankind an enduring supply of fuel that may be the most powerful and versatile source of energy ever known.

When Steve Nelson, now with the U.S. Naval Research Laboratory, was a nuclear astrophysics Ph.D. candidate at Duke University, he performed a calculation which shows that the impact of deuterium extraction from ocean water, for the purpose of generating fusion energy for the entire world's energy consumption, would lower the ocean surface only by one millimeter after several thousand years. Considering even the engineering inefficiencies and losses present in any power generation system, Earth's oceans have enough deuterium to last centuries.[1]

Electrolysis

One of the most common methods used to perform cold fusion experiments is that of electrolysis. Electrolysis is the process of passing an electrical current through a liquid, such as normal water (H_2O), and separating the hydrogen atoms from the oxygen atoms. In the case of heavy water (D_2O), deuterium atoms are separated from the oxygen atoms.

The basic cold fusion experiment is performed either in a small glass beaker, 250 milliliters in size, or in a narrow test tube, which can range from 20 to 100 milliliters in size. The difference in equipment varies based on the different methods of heat measurement employed.

In terms of its physical configuration and mechanical complexity, the apparatus is far less complex than the hot fusion apparatus. But a cold fusion electrolytic experiment is infinitely complex, deceptively so, on a smaller scale. Scientists must contend with a multitude of electrical, chemical, material science, metallurgical and time variables that all occur within the palladium cathode and the cell.

In the basic electrolytic cell, (Figure 1-2) an electrical circuit is made between the two poles of a battery and passed through a solution of liquid in a glass container. Two pieces of metal, or wires, are inserted into the container, one attached to the positive battery terminal, the other to the negative terminal.

Because pure water does not conduct electricity, the addition of salts to the liquid allows the electricity to flow through the solution, from one rod to the other. Lithium, in the form of LiOD, is a common salt used, as is potassium, in the form of K_2CO_3.

In a classical cold fusion electrolytic cell, platinum is usually connected to the positive terminal, palladium is usually connected to the negative terminal of the power source, and the heavy water solution is separated into its elemental components, deuterium and oxygen, by flow of current.

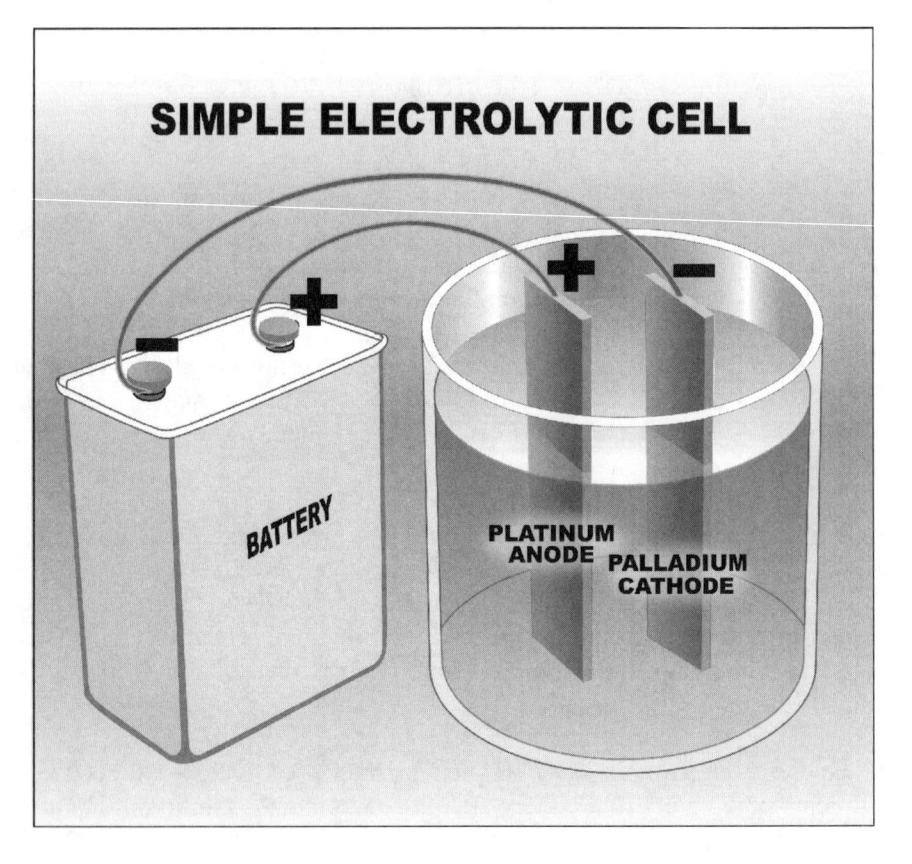

Figure 1-2. Simple Electrolytic Cell. (Drawing by Craig Erlick)

Calorimetry

The key effect that scientists seek in cold fusion experiments is the generation of large amounts of heat. This is the predominant reaction product from cold fusion and the most important for any potential commercial viability. The instrument to detect the presence of heat generation from cold fusion experiments is a calorimeter. A calorimeter measures heat. Just as a light bulb gives off heat when a current is passed through its filament, so does an electrolytic cell give off heat when current is passed through it. There are several types of calorimeters.

The critical piece in the cold fusion electrolytic experiment is the cathode. This is generally thought to be the site of the energy production, and it is submerged inside the cell. The energy emerges from the reaction between the metal cathode and the gaseous deuterium as heat, which in turn, causes the surrounding liquid to heat up. In order to measure the energy coming from the cell, one must be able to measure accurately this heat coming from the cell. This is the purpose of precision calorimetry.

Calorimetry is a complicated process and requires explicit skill and training. Generally, it is taught only in the field of physical chemistry, and even then, the occasions to use it are rare. Calorimetry is seldom taught in physics classes because physicists normally don't use calorimetry. This will turn out to be a major stumbling block for skeptical physicists trying to make sense of cold fusion.

The three types of calorimeters are isoperibolic, envelope-type, and mass-flow. Each has its strengths and weaknesses, but all require specialized skill. Figure 1-3 depicts the concept of the mass-flow type of calorimeter. The calorimeter surrounds the electrolytic cell in an independent jacket of water, much like the water that cools one's car engine. The water is made to flow continuously around the cold fusion cell. An electronic thermometer (thermistor) constantly measures the temperature going into the calorimeter, and another thermistor measures the water as it departs the calorimeter. The difference between these two readings and the flow rate of the surrounding water gives the amount of heat, or energy, being generated by the cell.

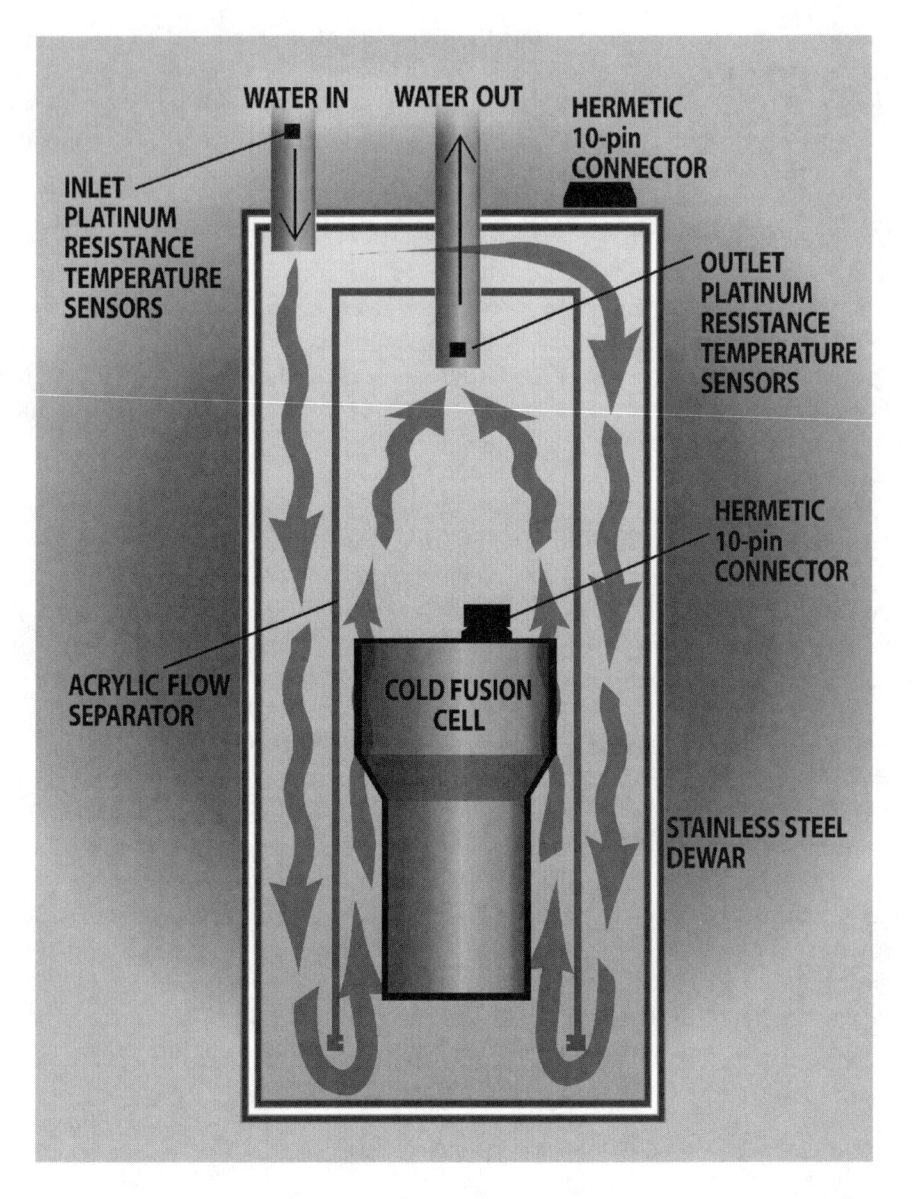

Figure1-3. SRI International-type Flow Calorimeter surrounding cold fusion cell. (Drawing by Craig Erlick)

Excess Heat

A fundamental principle in electrochemistry is that, when one places a certain amount of electrical energy through an electrolytic cell, one expects to get a commensurate amount of heat to come out of the cell.

For those who are mathematically inclined, this is represented in the following manner. If "Q" represents the amount of heat, "V" is the voltage, "I" is the current, and "t" is time, then $Q = V * I * t$.

In a standard electrolytic cell, the amount of energy coming out of the system is normally straightforward to calculate, using the above formula.

However, what Fleischmann and Pons discovered was that, in their cold fusion cell, Q, the amount of heat energy coming out of the cell, was much larger than it should have been based on any chemical reaction. An excessive amount of heat was coming from the experiment. It did not, in any way, match the amount of electrical energy going in plus other accounted-for energy losses! And this, in a nutshell, was their fundamental historic discovery: Something within the cell was releasing a new, "hitherto unknown" (Fleischmann-Pons) source of potential energy. In cold fusion research, this is the most important aspect of the phenomenon and is known by the term "excess heat."

How Cold Fusion Works

Figure 1-4 displays one of the most widely accepted models of the deuterium-deuterium cold fusion reaction. The nuclei (the center part of each atom) of two deuterium atoms, comprising a proton and neutron each, join together to form one helium-4 atom. Large amounts of heat also are given off as a result of the reaction.

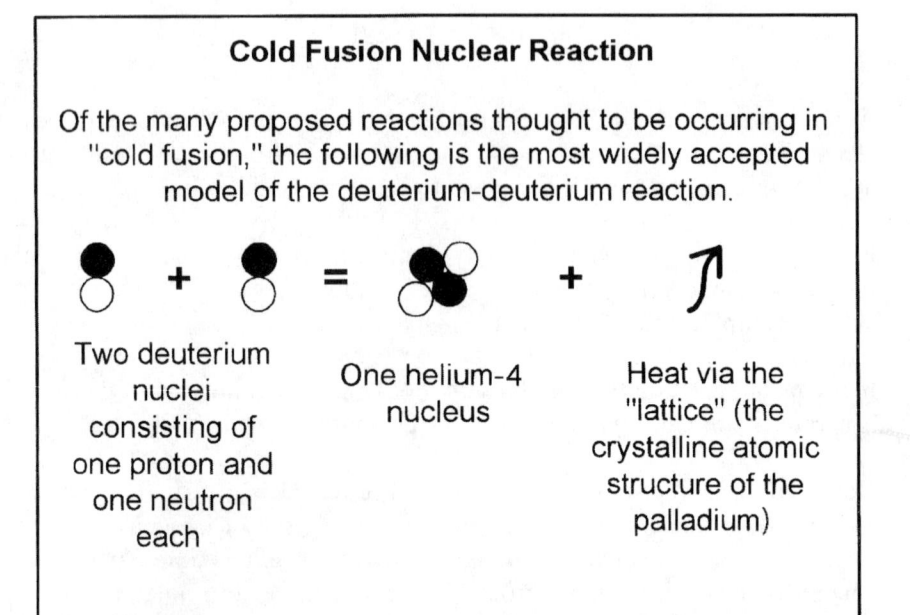

Figure 1-4. One Proposed Cold Fusion Nuclear Reaction

In contrast, *hot fusion's* normal byproducts are helium-3, tritium, and deadly neutron emissions. Only on rare occasions does helium-4, with its accompanying deadly gamma ray, appear in hot fusion. The results are, interestingly, almost reversed between hot and cold fusion, though both yield relatively large amounts of heat energy.

If the atomic masses of each proton/neutron pair are calculated, they equal slightly more than the atomic mass of the single helium-4 atom. This is where the liberated energy comes into the equation.

The difference in mass is accounted for by the portion of matter (deuterium) that has been converted into energy, which subsequently releases large amounts of heat. This heat is conveyed through the atoms of the palladium. The change in mass and subsequent conversion to energy are in accordance with Einstein's equation $E=mc^2$ and the law of conservation of mass-energy.

While many have claimed that cold fusion, once commercialized, will be an inexpensive source of energy, this may be somewhat optimistic. Certainly, deuterium, sold at retail for $1.00 per gram (much less in large quantities) is far less expensive as a nuclear fuel than uranium. However, "too cheap to meter," the catchphrase of nuclear fission plants, still rings in our ears. Dr. Edmund Storms, a radiochemist retired from the U.S. Los Alamos National Laboratory, said, "it's fair to say that the raw material is going to be cheaper than uranium, but we don't yet know how to make this work at a commercial level, and the costs for cold fusion power plants are a big unknown." [2]

Storms, who spent many years at Los Alamos working on nuclear energy systems for the space program, anticipates that cold fusion power plants, which likely will be small localized units, won't "have the safety problems which are inherent in nuclear fission plants." His reasoning, as discussed earlier, is that cold fusion appears to lack harmful radiation and radioactive waste and naturally will be simpler to build, far simpler than any hot fusion plant. "It's uncertain as to whether it would be less expensive than oil, but the raw material [deuterium] is certainly available in virtually unlimited quantities," Storms said.

Low Energy Nuclear Reactions (LENR)

A newer term has been adopted in recent years to classify a very broad set of experimental phenomena, which includes not only the classical heat-producing *cold fusion* experiments but also other interesting and anomalous reactions.

LENR refers to a variety of reactions that also occur in the presence of hydrogen- and deuterium-absorbing metals like palladium.

The cold fusion field is also known by other names and acronyms: CANR (Chemically Assisted Nuclear Reactions), CF (Cold Fusion), CNF (Cold Nuclear Fusion). CMNS (Condensed Matter Nuclear Science) also is evolving as the more scientific description for the entire field.

Readers wishing to see a more technical explanation of cold fusion will find "The Cold Fusion Effect: A Technical Explanation" at the end of Part Three.

CHAPTER TWO

Immense Hope and Skepticism

"Some say [cold] fusion may be man's greatest discovery since fire. Others say, as I do, that it may also be the innovation to protect and perpetuate the Earth's dying life support system, more important than the possible salvation of the dying industrial superiority of America. Man cannot stand another century like the last. In those 100 years, we have consumed more of the nonrenewable richness of the Earth than was used during all of man's previous history.

We polluted and poisoned our environment with its use, and it literally threatens our continued existence. The revolutionary discovery, [cold] fusion, arrives simultaneously with our entry into the age of true environmental alarm." [1]

--Congressman Wayne Owens, Utah, 1989 congressional
hearings on cold fusion

For many people, cold fusion represents hope as a way out of our terminal energy condition and our dependency on fossil fuels. Nevertheless, this very same hope causes much worry and concern for others. Reactions generating several watts of excess power (See Part Four, Power Densities) from cold fusion experiments have been shown to occur with equipment that is a fraction of the cost of that used in hot fusion research, and this bothers quite a few people, particularly those employed in the hot fusion field.

Those who are willing to accept the opinions of the world-class experts in the field who have studied cold fusion are bothered that billions of dollars have been spent on hot fusion without a single watt of useful power to show for it.

Others, who have not studied cold fusion and who have, to date, refused to do so, are bothered because a new scientific paradigm such as cold fusion runs counter to their beliefs about the world and about science. For nuclear physicists, cold fusion contradicts a majority of what they have learned throughout most of their professional lives.

The fuel deuterium is one of the few similarities between hot fusion and cold fusion. However, the most significant difference is that cold fusion produces no harmful radiation. Cold fusion produces no greenhouse gasses or deadly neutrons, only helium, which is environmentally safe. Helium does not contribute to global warming. It is safe enough for children to play with in balloons or, when slightly devious, to inhale it from the balloons and talk like a chipmunk.

These amazingly positive qualities of cold fusion bring tremendous hope to some - and tremendous concern to others.

Far and away, the biggest problem with the hypothesis of cold fusion is that *it sounds too good to be true!* If cold fusion turns out to be what it seems, it will be nothing short of a miracle, in fact several miracles combined into one: abundant energy, pollution-free energy, nearly unlimited energy and possibly very low-cost energy, not to mention several of the technical "miracles" its naysayers have mocked in arrogant and ignorant disbelief.

In addition, if cold fusion succeeds, the odds are quite good that scarcities of many kinds will cease to exist. The ability to transport water great distances to irrigate barren lands may support agriculture for starving nations. The ability to desalinate ocean water cost-effectively may provide unlimited quantities of life-essential drinking water that in some countries is more precious than oil.

If cold fusion can be commercialized, new modes of transportation, using magnetic levitation technology and others beyond our imagination, will become possible. The cost of energy, an integral part of every product and service, may be reduced to a fraction of its current cost. The social, political,

14

financial and economic implications are mind-boggling, to borrow the favorite term of Dr. Eugene Mallove, founder of Infinite Energy magazine and cold fusion advocate. Other speculative views of the possible impact of cold fusion technology are discussed in Part Four.

Which brings us to the real and only valid question regarding cold fusion now: Can it be scaled up? The energy that is generated in cold fusion experiments does not come out as electrical energy. The energy is released from the experiments as *heat energy* and must go through a conversion process before it can be used as electricity. Today's best converters achieve only 30 percent efficiency.

This means that, if a cold fusion cell produces 100 watts of generated heating power, it will yield only 30 watts of electrical power using the best converter available today. To obtain usable amounts of electrical energy, cold fusion will have to generate at least three times more energy than is being applied to the device in order to be cost-effective when the resulting heat is converted into electricity

This is not such bad news. Computer technology, for instance, has seen increases in processor speed and storage capacity in many orders of magnitude over recent decades. If governments and industry fast-tracked cold fusion, this research, currently financed on a shoestring and personal retirement funds, might show similar progress.

Cold fusion's ability to be scaled up is the trillion-dollar question - and will determine whether this, like hot fusion, will ever be more than a scientific curiosity.

Other technical questions and breakthroughs remain to be solved, such as how to prepare the metals in the cells so that they turn on every time and how to prevent corrosion (which halts the reactions) from accumulating.

Just this sort of bold optimism irks cynics and causes knee-jerk reactions of disgust and mistrust by those who consider such a promise to be a delusion, an altruistic fantasy. In the field of cold fusion, we find that, as in other areas of life, the cynics scoff and sneer. True skeptics, however, remain undecided while they actively inquire and investigate. There is certainly reason to be skeptical, but not to be cynical.

Not a day goes by without consumers being sold something new – a new type of electronic device, for example, purported to be simple to install - that invariably requires the services of a specialist to finish the job, at great cost. Alternatively, one may purchase a seat in a class that claims to teach methods which are sure to lead one to wealth in the stock market, yet that too brings disappointment.

Patience for so-called revolutionary technologies has worn thin. In 2001, newspapers heralded a mysterious new transportation device, leading with the question, "Could it really change the world?" The hype continued with celebrity quotes and rumors of a hefty book advance describing the invention. We were even bedazzled with a code name: Ginger.

We were told that Ginger would revolutionize personal transportation and that cities would re-design themselves to accommodate this new mode of transportation. Three years later, the $4,000 U.S. electric scooter called the Segway has not, in any way, changed the world. Few, if any, cities have taken steps to accommodate the device, and starting with San Francisco, some have even initiated outright bans on the "revolutionary" device.

Virtually nothing comes to consumers without a certain amount of hype and marketing spin, and sadly and far too often, the advertising is deceptive. Cold fusion appears to fit precisely the common maxim, "If it sounds too good to be true, it probably is," and as such, it should call forth great caution from skeptical, astute observers new to this subject.

Nobody likes having the wool pulled over their eyes, least of all in a highly specialized subject where an ordinary person can't verify the claims without extensive training and a very sophisticated suite of diagnostic instruments. Therefore, a healthy, honest skepticism is warranted.

Cold fusion is clearly a paradox. On the one hand, it is so far beyond belief to a few outspoken scientists that they denounce this entire field, en masse, as folly and foolishness.

On the other hand, more quiet-spoken scientists, with equivalent backgrounds and training (but perhaps less social and political stature), have inquired into the subject. They have read the published papers in peer-review-journals; they have contacted the originators of the work and sorted out for themselves whether the authors' procedures meet their expectations for good science. Some also have visited labs to see the experiments firsthand.

They are fully aware that they tread in treacherous waters, for a matter as promising as cold fusion calls for the utmost care and scrutiny. And after performing such due diligence, they have been persuaded that the dramatic findings of Fleischmann and Pons, the excess heat effect, is as real as any other phenomenon known to science.

Cold fusion is indeed a fascinating scientific phenomenon, but one cannot see it with the naked eye, nor can just any scientist see it without experience in electrochemistry and specific training in calorimetry. No one wants to be fooled by overly optimistic scientists or by those who may be blinded by their own altruism or ego.

Some nuclear physicists likely will feel a certain responsibility to society to protect others from what they might believe is fraud or foolishness. After all, for more than half a century, they have been the experts in nuclear power, as have been their teachers and their teachers' teachers.

Many skeptical experts are convinced that the cold fusion phenomenon is all the result of experimental error. It is reasonable to assume that these skeptics are caring individuals and would not want to see their fellow citizens snookered by unscrupulous charlatans who ask for money to fund their presumably erroneous projects. It also would enrage them to see public trust in science abused - in their view.

As a caveat to any person who has sufficient technical background to understand nuclear physics thoroughly, please take the following under consideration: While the authors hope this book will awaken your curiosity and interest, this book will not provide the depth and details necessary for a thorough scientific evaluation. The authors know that such an evaluator will need to see graphs, error bars, and signal-to-noise ratios. The person will need to see an accounting of conservation of mass, energy and momentum and results of control studies, among other details. Such a person is respectfully directed to the following sources of information:

- The 2004 Department of Energy cold fusion review summary paper, "New Physical Effects in Metal Deuterides," by Peter L. Hagelstein (MIT), Michael C.H. McKubre (SRI International), David J. Nagel (The George Washington University), Talbot A. Chubb (Research Systems Inc.), Randall J. Hekman (Hekman Industries). This paper presented research from 130 selected papers to those involved with the review and is available at www.newenergytimes.com.

- *"Excess Heat & Why Cold Fusion Research Prevailed, Second Edition"* by Charles G. Beaudette published in 2002 by Oak Grove Press, LLC in South Bristol, Maine, USA, (ISBN 0-9678548-30) is a virtual encyclopedia of cold fusion history, methodology, and research.

- The Web site www.lenr-canr.org (Low Energy Nuclear Reactions - Chemically Assisted Nuclear Reactions), hosted by Jed Rothwell and Edmund Storms provides an easy-to-use bibliography of thousands of cold fusion papers. Several hundred of them are available for download directly at the site.

- The International Conference on Cold Fusion series, also known as the International Conference on Condensed Matter Nuclear Science, is an excellent place to listen and directly interact with many of the scientists who are active in the field.

- Regional yearly cold fusion conferences are also held in Japan, Russia and Italy.

The International Conference on Cold Fusion has been held every 12 to 16 months since 1990. Details for these conferences can be found at the Web site www.newenergytimes.com. Presentations also are regularly given at meetings of the American Physical Society and the American Nuclear Society.

CHAPTER THREE

Fuel Scarcity and *Climate Change*

Emissions from fossil fuels now foul Earth's oceans and the entire planet's atmosphere. Humankind's balance of power is inextricably tied to, and dependent on, one dreadful coincidence: Our last great petroleum reserves are located in some of our least stable regions. The First World's dependency on Third World oil places everyone at great peril. And the only viable large-scale alternative at present, conventional nuclear power, comes at great financial and environmental cost.

Energy, like the air we breathe and the food we eat, is an essential part of daily survival. Every aspect of life is dependent on energy, from the heat in our homes, to the irrigation of our crops, to the manufacture of every product in every store. Regardless of which country we live in, energy is a precious and essential commodity.

Yet the fossil fuels we rely on for energy are starting to show real signs of scarcity. David Goodstein, California Institute of Technology vice provost and professor of physics, wrote in his book, *Out of Gas*, "civilization as we know it will not survive, unless we can find a way to live without fossil fuels."

The fact that we will run out of gas is undeniable, though exactly when is subject to debate. This end of oil has been predicted since the 1950s by geophysicist M. King Hubbert and has been demonstrated since the 1970s, when the United States reached its conventional peak oil production capability. The United States has seen a steady decline since then. This concern has become known as both Peak Oil and the Hubbert Peak.

The Association for the Study of Peak Oil, comprising oil executives, geologists, and even investment bankers, has been warning the world of a future of higher oil prices as total peak oil production occurs sometime around 2010 and new sizeable oil discoveries in various forms start to decline.[1]

According to geologist Kenneth S. Deffeyes of Princeton University, the global oil reserves may *already* have reached peak production. In a November 2001 presentation at the Geological Society of America annual meeting, Deffeyes wrote that the most optimistic estimate is that global peak oil would occur in 2004 and the least optimistic estimate for a world Hubbert peak would be in 2002. He made an additional point:

> The largest single uncertainty is the enormous reserves in Saudi Arabia, due to the fact that the Saudis remain secretive as to the exact status of their future capacities.

This major uncertainty, however, is starting to become clear. Saudi Arabia, known for having the world's largest oil reserves, may have reached its peak oil production. Figure 1-5 displays one of the many available statistics that illuminate the projected depletion of oil and natural gas resources worldwide.

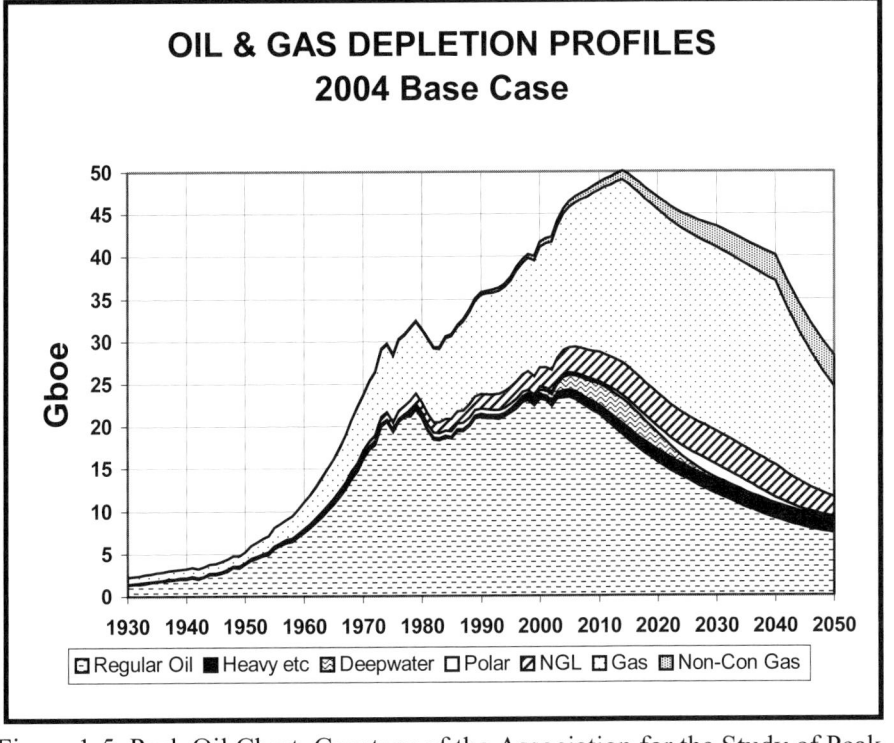

Figure 1-5. Peak Oil Chart, Courtesy of the Association for the Study of Peak Oil. GBOE = Billion Barrels Oil Equivalent.

The New York Times reported on Feb. 24, 2004, "Saudi Arabia's vast oil fields, pumped for more than a half-century, are in decline." The article continued, apparently in an effort to defray panic, "Saudi Arabia is not running out of oil, but it is becoming more difficult or expensive to extract." According to a report in the June 2004 *National Geographic*, Saudi technical reports indicate that some fields are coming up with water instead of oil.[2]

To the north, in the European continent, Shell Oil Company shocked its investors weeks earlier on Jan. 9, 2004, when it reduced its estimates for its proven oil and gas reserves by 20 percent, as reported by The New York Times the following day.

Additional signs are emerging. In 2001, the defense think tank RAND Corporation, which helped germinate the modern Internet and space satellites, published a report titled "Environmental Implications of Population Dynamics." This report summarized a vast amount of statistical evidence showing how the human population is placing an increasing burden on our global environment. And, you guessed it, there is an increasing need for energy, with no end in sight.[3]

As underdeveloped nations move up in socioeconomic status, so do their demands for energy from fossil fuels. The RAND authors explained:

> Compared with human-induced environmental changes of centuries past, the geographic scope of contemporary human induced change is much larger. The rate of change is much larger. ... Population-oriented policies represent only one of many routes through which modern societies must respond to human-induced environmental decline.

Perhaps renewed interest in fundamental energy research is one alternative to such policies. The U.S. Department of Energy, with a long-standing pattern of neglect for funding alternative means of energy research, often can miss projections. However, it recently changed its views. In a recent report titled "International Energy Outlook 2004," the Department of Energy's Energy Information Agency clearly pointed out that the required per capita energy needs of developing countries far exceed the capacity of underdeveloped countries: [4]

> Because economic growth rates and population growth in the developing world are expected to be higher than in the industrialized world, accompanied by rising standards of living and fast-paced growth in energy-intensive industries, the developing nations account for the largest share of the projected increase in world energy use. Emissions are projected to grow most rapidly in China, the country expected to have the highest rate of growth in per capita income and fossil fuel use over the forecast period.

Even this conservative Department of Energy report missed projections on the current price of a barrel of crude, which as of this writing hovers around $42 a barrel. A bit earlier than the 2025 date this report projects, indeed.

This looming crisis in both population growth and its environmental consequences for energy demands will have far-reaching effects on the economies of all developed nations and the products they sell, which demand more and more energy in various forms. With the peak oil issue, general population trends, global warming and the increasing global energy needs, this century will witness radical changes in all aspects of energy and sustainability.

In the past, it seemed we often had unlimited oil supplies and a stable environment. But this is no longer true. For those who are not yet alarmed, do not think major regions of the earth remain to be explored. Even the vast Bitumen oil sand regions of Canada are much harder to extract than flowing crude from conventional wells and will do little to tame the growing Third World thirst for fuel.

Experts note that we have pinpricked this ball named Earth in nearly every conceivable spot, and what we see of the known oil reserves is just about all we get.

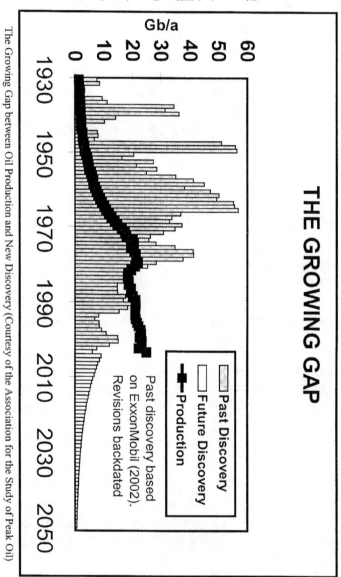

THE GROWING GAP

Gb/a

Past Discovery
Future Discovery
Production

Past discovery based
on ExxonMobil (2002).
Revisions backdated

Figure 1-6 "The Growing Gap"

The Growing Gap between Oil Production and New Discovery (Courtesy of the Association for the Study of Peak Oil)

Global Warming

Inextricably tied to global energy use is the concern of "global warming." While the subject of much debate in recent years, the issue has many experts worried.

The problem of global warming predominantly results from the combustion of fossil fuels. According to the U.S. Environmental Protection Agency, "fossil fuels burned to run cars and trucks, heat homes and businesses, and power factories are responsible for about 98 percent of U.S. carbon dioxide emissions, 24 percent of methane emissions, and 18 percent of nitrous oxide emissions." These are the so-called "greenhouse gasses."

Carbon dioxide is the greatest culprit. It is odorless and invisible; for the most part, it does its damage without our awareness. Carbon dioxide and other greenhouse gasses collect in the upper part of the Earth's atmosphere and remain trapped there. When solar radiation passes through the Earth's atmosphere, most of this radiation is absorbed by the earth's surface. However, some of the solar radiation is reflected back to the atmosphere. Ordinarily, part of this radiation would continue onward to outer space, and part would be reflected back to earth.

However, as a blanket of greenhouse gasses accumulates in the upper atmosphere, it absorbs the wavelengths of reflected radiation and converts it into thermal energy. The gasses remains trapped, upsetting the delicate energy balance as the Earth makes its yearly journey around the sun, and contributing to an increase in global temperature worldwide.

The U.S. Environmental Protection Agency said this about the threat of global warming:

> Rising global temperatures are expected to raise sea levels, and change precipitation and other local climate conditions. Changing regional climates could alter forests, crop yields, and water supplies. It could also affect human health, animals, and many types of ecosystems. Deserts may expand into existing rangelands, and features of some of our National Parks may be permanently altered.[5]

As reported in the January 2002 Scientific American by Daniel Grossman, the 2002 Intergovernmental Panel on Climate Change reviewed 2,500 published reports and papers and reported on the relationship of life pattern changes in the world's plants and animals to temperature changes over the last 20 years. The authors of the report found "a discernible impact of regional climate change, particularly increases in temperature, on biological systems in the 20th century." [6]

While some scientists disagree with the imminence of the global warming threat, much of the optimism seems based on a belief that the world will find alternatives to fossil fuels before the worst-case scenario is on us. The problem with this belief, however, is that most scientists indicate that we are, optimistically, half a century away from the widespread application of any radically new energy technology.

The Limits of Current Energy Sources

As reported by Kenneth Chang in the Nov. 4, 2003, issue of *The New York Times*, 85 percent of today's worldwide demand for energy is delivered through the consumption of fossil fuels: coal, natural gas, and oil. Hydroelectric provides 6.5 percent, but it is a finite resource and is, for the most part, maximized. Nuclear fission also provides 6.5 percent of the world's energy. The renewable energy sources, wind and solar, so far have shown to be ineffective for large-scale energy production; they supply 2 percent of the world's energy needs. [7]

Fossil fuels are the largest sources of energy at the world's disposal. These energy sources are nonrenewable: Once they are pumped, refined, distributed and consumed, they are gone forever.

There is another key fact regarding all fossil fuels: They are examples of chemical energy processes. Fossil fuels release energy through combustion, a chemical process which releases heat, light and combustion products. From the perspective of science, these energy sources are more or less indistinguishable from the simple wood-burning fire used by cave men for millennia. A piece of wood ignites and burns, and heat, light, carbon dioxide and ash result.

The energy density, or the amount of chemical energy contained in a quantity of fossil fuel, is given by the thermodynamics of the chemical reaction. Chemical combustion has been pushed to its limits to obtain useful work.

Admittedly, coal, natural gas, and gasoline are much more convenient and somewhat more energetic than wood for our energy needs, but they all yield quantities of energy within a similar range, which is far, far less than any kind of nuclear power source.

CHAPTER FOUR

Nuclear Fission: A Mixed Blessing

Since the early 1960s, nuclear power plants have been in operation and have provided energy around the world. In 1979, a partial actual meltdown at a nuclear power plant in Three Mile Island, Pennsylvania, resulted in thousands of injuries from radiation. And in 1986, the Chernobyl Nuclear Power Plant in the Ukraine endured a chemical explosion which exposed nearly 8.5 million people to radiation, official reports said, over a territory almost half the size of Italy.

The public has developed a disdain for nuclear energy. Perhaps this is somewhat unfounded, given the newer, safer reactor technologies available. A short lesson in the history of nuclear fission will provide a better understanding of this energy source.

The term "nuclear fission" was coined around 1939 by Lise Meitner and Otto Frisch.[1] From their work and the work of Otto Hahn and Fritz Strassmann, Italian physicist Enrico Fermi envisioned the possibility of obtaining a chain reaction.

In 1939, Fermi, having immigrated to the United States to escape the war in Europe, was at Columbia University in New York when he received word from future Nobel laureate and physics colleague Willis Lamb of the successful bombardment of uranium by neutrons.[2]

In a world that was in many ways much simpler than today's, stories of science discoveries were as exciting then as were the initial public offerings during the crazed Internet boom of the late 1990s. In the 1930s and 1940s, news within the science community spread more directly, in a person-to-person fashion, as scientists eagerly awaited news of scientific discoveries from their peers.[3]

Following the exciting news of uranium bombardment, two teams, including Fermi in New York, observed neutrons being liberated during the process of fission.[4] Fermi and his colleagues had developed a firm grasp of fission theory at the time. The idea of a controllable fission reactor soon started to take shape, and Fermi and others saw an emerging opportunity.

He and a team of colleagues under Army Major Gen. Leslie R. Groves relocated to the University of Chicago after the Defense Department established the U.S. Army's Manhattan Engineering District to help build the first atomic "pile," as it was called.[5] It comprised uranium oxide pellets, graphite bricks and a custom-built square balloon bag for sealing the pile in a partial vacuum.

As the humorous side of the story goes, the Goodyear Tire and Rubber Company specialists who received the order couldn't imagine why the U.S. Army would spend money on a square balloon. This balloon was the butt of many jokes at the time.

On Dec. 2, 1942, the dream of controlled nuclear power was born. As physicist Arthur Compton later relayed by phone, the Italian "navigator" (Fermi) and talented colleagues had landed in the new world, as they demonstrated the first controlled nuclear chain reaction in this simple atomic pile. It was a painstaking endeavor, carried out in secret. After they had succeeded, the Chicago team drank, then autographed a bottle of Chianti as they celebrated.

Controlled nuclear fission is a process in which a larger element is split into two smaller elements, simultaneously releasing energy and several neutrons that continue the reaction. Years later, after more engineering research and development, reactors were designed to convert heated water to steam and turn electric turbines, producing the first nuclear-generated electricity. This fission process also produced radioactive waste and a variety of radiation, with significant environmental consequences.

Figure 1-7 shows an example of nuclear fission. Once a neutron strikes a uranium-235 atom, prompt fission occurs, and the uranium nucleus, the center of the atom, becoming unstable, quickly splits apart into unequal pieces. Dozens of reaction pathways are possible, such as one that yields xenon-140 and strontium-94, along with two neutrons. Other pathways may release three neutrons. Released neutrons can either be absorbed (a new fission occurs), or they can escape to the surface of the reactor (a loss).

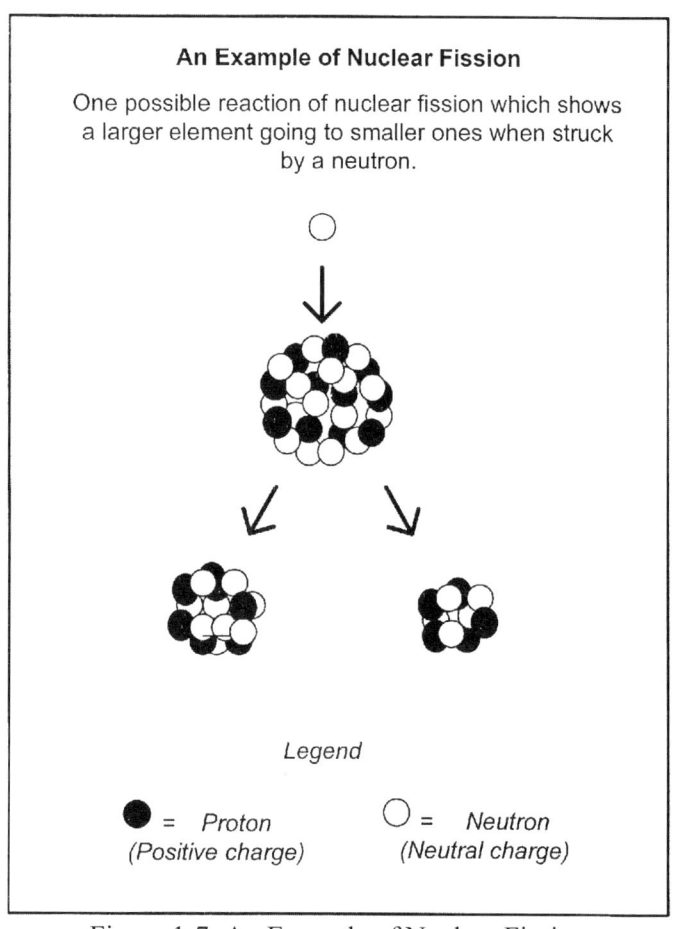

Figure 1-7. An Example of Nuclear Fission

The process of splitting atoms yields large amounts of energy, and this is the current method by which nuclear reactors operate. This contrasts with nuclear weaponry, which relies on the rapid release of energy in an explosion.

The idea of controlled nuclear fission was very exciting when it was developed. Ideas and applications ranged from powering ships and aircraft to electric power stations. It was indeed promising, with the amount of energy produced from one pound of uranium equivalent to that of the combustion of 10,000 pounds of coal or oil.

Since the early days, nuclear fission plants have been a mixed blessing. "Too cheap to meter" was the oft-heard catchphrase. Sadly, "too cheap to meter" turned into "too expensive to build and dispose of the hazardous waste."

Nuclear-powered aircraft ideas in the early 1950s were abandoned because of technical challenges and weight. However, in 1951, at a reactor site in Idaho, the first 100 kilowatts of electricity were produced. Spurred on by this mixed success, in 1954, the Atoms for Peace program of U.S. President Eisenhower allowed private companies to own nuclear reactors. Following this announcement, the U.S. Atomic Energy Commission provided research and development programs to help private industry use nuclear power with proper regulations.

Westinghouse and General Electric built demonstration reactors for the Navy and were quite successful. On Aug. 10, 1955, electricity from a nuclear submarine was used to demonstrate electric power generation. In a public demonstration, the electricity was used to cook hamburgers on a common electric stove. Two years later, the Shippingport Nuclear Power Station, the world's first commercial nuclear power plant, came online. It brought with it 60 megawatts of electricity, enough to turn on the lights in 100,000 homes.[6]

The evolution from the Chicago pile to the first 60 megawatts took *15 years* of continual research and development, sponsored and nurtured by government dollars and private industry participation.

Since 1957, the engineering and construction costs of nuclear power plants have been immense and problematic at times. No easy solution has been found for storage of the radioactive spent nuclear fuel rods. Daniel B. Wood wrote in his *Christian Science Monitor* article, "Along nuclear reactor's path, cries of 'NIMBY (Not In My Back Yard)'"; nobody wants this deadly waste in his or her backyard.[7]

Waste from power plants of various levels is hermetically sealed and buried underground. Keeping long-term radioactive waste safe and secure, at the cost of many billions of dollars, is not cheap.

France, a country that draws 75 percent of its power from nuclear fission, has had an excellent track record with its 58 power plants. Other countries, such as the United States and Russia, have not been so lucky.[8] By letting other nations lead the way, the French hedged their bets and learned from the mistakes of others. Their stable regulatory environment and funding approach allowed them to produce electricity at 4 cents per kilowatt-hour, compared to the U.S. range of 7.5 cents per kilowatt-hour and higher.

Accidents such as those at Chernobyl and Three Mile Island confirmed the world's fears of the operational dangers of nuclear fission plants based on old-style fission technologies. The radioactivity released from the Chernobyl accident in Russia alone is known to have traveled across Europe, poisoning food and water, and it is also likely to have entered the food chain. Since then, the public fear of this industry has been inextricably linked to environmental issues.

All countries that produce nuclear fission energy must face the inevitable problem of storing highly toxic radioactive waste for hundreds of years, as well as contending with the risk of terrorist attacks on such high-profile targets. Securing this waste in a safe manner is paramount, and it is expensive. Numerous safety risks for plant workers, the community and the environment remain.

Environmental problems are the human legacy of the 20th century, whether related to the carbon dioxide emissions of fossil fuels or the hazardous storage of nuclear waste products.

Despite the environmental consequences, nuclear research has helped humankind. Medical and other scientific spin-off applications have occurred, as well as the production of many megawatts of electricity.

In what appears to be an acknowledgment of the dire predictions of oil scarcity, the U.S. Department of Energy recently took the very unpopular step of beginning construction on the first new nuclear fission power plant in decades. As expected, many environmentalists are opposed to this approach.

The traditional environmentally-conscious view, however, may be changing. Even famed environmentalist James Lovelock has called for increased use of atomic energy to help reduce fossil fuel consumption and greenhouse gases. He stated the following in a May 24, 2004, interview on a Australian Broadcasting Company program:

> Every day we're putting more and more carbon dioxide into the air, and we're, in a sense, almost past the point of no return already, as far as our descendants are concerned. If we just go on like this, we're going to leave them an utterly impoverished world, and I don't think any of us wants to do that.[9]

Lovelock replied to reporter Kirsten Aiken's questions by advocating increased use of nuclear power, potentially shocking many people in the green movement:

> I understand their reservations and fears. But it's a matter of comparative dangers. If you are threatened with some unpleasant disease, you often have to take medicines with unpleasant side effects, and one should look on nuclear in that sense. We don't have any alternative. I wish we did.

Recently, U.S. Secretary of Energy Spencer Abraham stated the following in a May 23, 2004, press release:

> Nuclear [fission] power is the only large-scale source of domestically produced electricity that does not produce greenhouse gases. It is, therefore, one of our most important energy sources today and has tremendous potential to support the nation's energy and environmental goals in the future.

Clearly, this is the direction the United States and much of the world has chosen to power this planet into the 21st century, mostly as an alternative to none. Many scientists dream of a better alternative.

CHAPTER FIVE

The Overextended Promise of Hot Fusion

For 50 years, gifted scientists around the world have had as their best hope the dream of harnessing energy from thermonuclear fusion.

While thermonuclear fusion occurs naturally in the core of the sun and the stars, it is not so easy to achieve on the surface of the Earth. Thermonuclear fusion is also known as "hot fusion," or "plasma fusion," referring to the superheated gas-like state in which such experiments occur.

Whereas nuclear *fission*, described in the last chapter, is simply the splitting of atoms, *fusion* is the joining of atoms to obtain a release of energy.

Figure 1-8 shows an example of one of the various reaction paths that occur in hot fusion. Generally, smaller elements, such as various forms of hydrogen, join to create larger elements, such as helium-3.

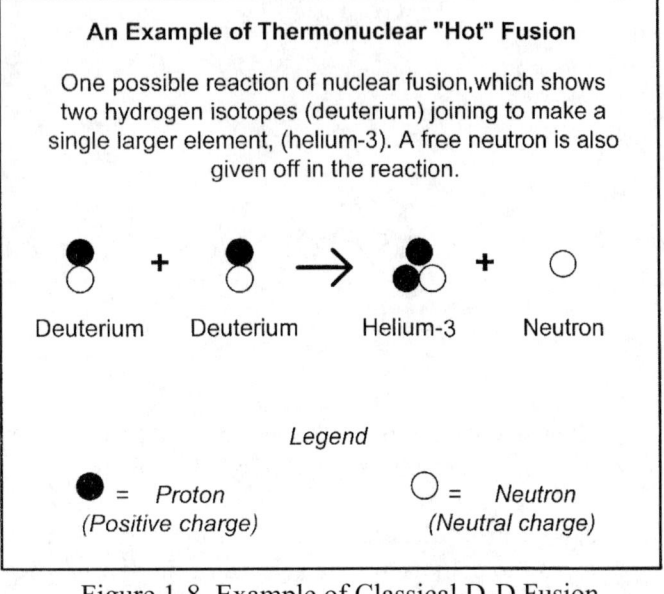

Figure 1-8. Example of Classical D-D Fusion

Fusion's Features and Benefits

The concept of thermonuclear fusion as a power source is attractive because it is free of combustion products and greenhouse gases. Because of hot fusion's absence of nuclear waste and long-term radiation, it has appeared to conventional scientists to be the Holy Grail of energy research. If commercially effective, fusion, either the hot or cold kind, eventually would make any technology based on the burning of fossil fuels, that is, hydrocarbons, obsolete. Radiation in thermonuclear "hot" fusion is only minimal compared to fission, but the amount is still deadly to humans if protection systems fail.[1]

Many scientists (as well as government funding agencies) are dedicated to fusion research because, aside from nuclear fission, it appears to be the only long-range solution accepted by conventional science that offers a possible exit from the dead end of fossil fuels. There is no debate about whether fusion on earth is possible. The debate is whether it will be economically practical, on what scale, and when?

Theoretically, thermonuclear fusion has the potential for far greater energy production than anything remotely possible from fossil fuel sources, or even nuclear fission. For example, compared to chemical energy, if one burns two atoms of hydrogen in combustion, the energy from the same two atoms in a fusion reaction would yield 8 million times the amount of energy from the same quantity of hydrogen.[2]

Achieving commercial and even scientific success with thermonuclear fusion has been challenging. Nuclear physicists traditionally have thought that fusion requires temperatures in the millions of degrees to make atoms collide and fuse together. Achieving these temperatures on earth is no easy trick and would be considered by scientists to be a technological miracle should it eventually succeed. Scientists have attempted to recreate such extreme temperatures on Earth by one of two primary means: using arrays of enormous lasers in inertial confinement fusion, and using immense magnetic confinement fusion machines known as "Tokamak" machines.

In contrast to cold fusion, which occurs in a piece of metal, hot fusion occurs in the free space of an empty tokamak chamber. The release of the heat is carried away by neutrons, tritium, and proton ions. X-rays and occasionally gamma rays also occur as a result of neutron activation of the surrounding material.

Magnetically Confined Fusion

Magnetic confinement methods are one way to release the intense heat energy from fusion reactions and, when harnessed to turn electric turbines or to produce electricity directly, provide power to perform useful work.

Originally developed in the Soviet Union, a "Tokamak," a Russian acronym, is a magnetic chamber containing superconducting magnetic field coils. When seen from the inside, it looks like a large doughnut- shaped machine and can be as large as a three-story house. Not all Tokamaks are alike. For instance, in the versions which burn a deuterium tritium mixture, radioactive tritium also can escape, so adequate safeguards must be taken for health protection. Tokamak designs using deuterium fuel exclusively would be the ideal form of fusion for safety reasons, but the power yield is less than those burning the deuterium tritium fuel. Deuterium (only) fusion Tokamaks have been tried for a number of years with mixed results.

According to Anthony R. DeMeo of the Princeton Plasma Physics Laboratory in the United States, the closest Princeton has ever come to just "breaking even," where the amount of generated power would equal the amount of input power, is only 27 percent. In other words, only 27 percent of input power was produced in fusion. The tokamak called the Joint European Torus in the United Kingdom has fared better, but that unit, too, has generated, at its best, only 60 percent of the input power it consumed.[3] Some proponents like to calculate that, if the experiments were run with tritium as well as deuterium, they may have reached "break-even," but this is speculative. After 50 years, hot fusion still chases the elusive break-even breakthrough.

With enough time and money, hot fusion scientists are hopeful that they will overcome this and other remaining challenges. In the United States, at least, Congress' patience is wearing thin. Doubting whether a new U.S. program under construction will ever create more energy than it consumes, one member of Congress recently expressed strong doubts that such a program will ever achieve ignition. "You know, how I feel right now is that I've been hoodwinked," Sen. Pete Domenici told executives of the U.S. National Nuclear Security Administration in March 2004.[4]

Inertially Confined Fusion

Www.hypertexbook.com says, "The largest and most powerful laser in the world is the NOVA laser. It is located at the Lawrence Livermore National Laboratory in California. The NOVA laser is about as long as a football field and is three stories high."[5] Programs such as the National Ignition Facility are expanding and improving on the work of the NOVA design. Inertial confinement fusion hopes to achieve ignition by compressing tiny pellets of deuterium with energy from lasers to achieve break-even conditions. Scaling up from the NOVA design is expected to provide this capability.

Attaining break-even is the first major technical hurdle for hot fusion. Even if "ignition" is achieved, that still doesn't mean that an answer to energy problems is at hand. From there, hot fusion must overcome several other critical engineering breakthroughs before it becomes a commercial reality.

The optimistic estimate for when a hot fusion *experiment* will produce more energy than it consumes is 2010 to 2015. From there, the remaining required breakthroughs are expected to take another 40 years of research. Not until 2050 does the hot fusion industry expect to bring its first commercial fusion power plant online to plug into the public power grid and generate its first megawatt.

Fusion Funding

In the United States, hot fusion research began at Princeton University in 1951 through a U.S. military program. With development of the hydrogen bomb well under way at the time, having a power-generating fusion reactor within a decade seemed quite optimistic. In 1958, the first director of the U.S. Fusion program, Amasa S. Bishop, agreed:

> With ingenuity, hard work, and a sprinkling of good luck, it even seems reasonable to hope that full-scale power-producing thermonuclear devices may be built within the next decade or two.

Five decades of research and billions of taxpayer dollars later, not a single commercial plant has been built; nor has one single watt of excess energy been produced from these experiments. In fact, $16 billion later, (Figure 1-9) these experiments require so much electricity just to run that they consume more energy than they produce.

Dr. David Nagel, research professor at The George Washington University and fusion physicist who worked for 36 years at the U.S. Naval Research Laboratory, described his graph, based on data obtained from the U.S. Department of Energy:

> The broader, shorter lines are the then-year dollars. The narrower, taller lines are adjusted for inflation as of the year 2000, which amounts to a grand total of $16.4 billion.

It basically shows three phases. Once thermonuclear plasma fusion became declassified around 1950, the program ran along more or less flat. Then we had the OPEC oil crisis in 1973, and it jumped up. After that, it has just gradually tailed off.[6]

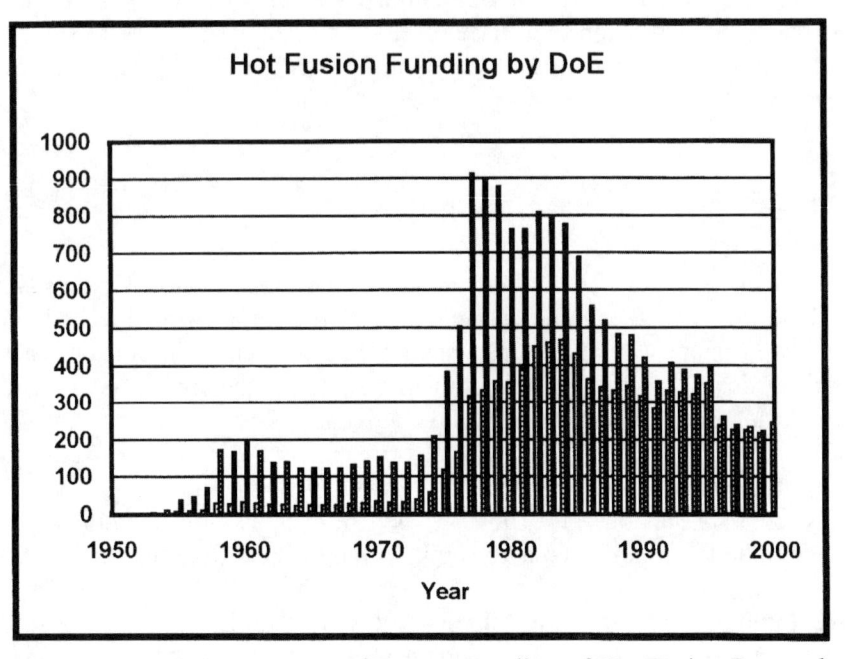

Figure 1-9. U.S. Department of Energy Funding of Hot Fusion Research Since 1950.

The prime years of U.S. hot fusion funding appear to have peaked. In its place, many of the U.S. and world's nuclear physicists recently have set all hopes on the International Thermonuclear Experimental Reactor.

The costs and complexities of this project are so immense that many countries decided to pool their resources to work cooperatively to solve the continuing hot fusion puzzle. At the time of this writing, the immediate challenge facing the International Thermonuclear Experimental Reactor is not technical but political: Half of the participant countries wish to see the reactor built in France; the other half want it built in Japan.

The quiet word from some physicists, however, is that, if the International Thermonuclear Experimental Reactor represents the enormous size and complexity of fusion energy, power companies are unlikely to be interested. And building this device wherever power is needed is impractical.

Whether conventional hot fusion will turn out to be the answer to the planet's needs for a viable alternative to fossil fuels is highly uncertain. Dr. Robert Park, spokesman for the American Physical Society, said the following about hot fusion programs in general:

> It turned out to be much harder than we thought, but they make steady progress. It's not spectacular progress, but the joke is it's the energy source of the future and it always will be, because they're constantly giving you an estimate of how many years before we have controlled fusion reactors in business and it doesn't happen.[7]

Judy Franz, executive officer of the American Physical Society, is more optimistic about hot fusion:

> This is the kind that physicists believe in and that definitely works. ... I think most people think eventually this will be a major source of energy. The question is when and how.[8]

CHAPTER SIX

The Limited Promise of Hydrogen

Politicians and some industry pundits have touted hydrogen as the future replacement for fossil fuels.

Plain and simple, hydrogen is not an energy source. It is an energy carrier, a storage medium. It can be used as a fuel, but the element hydrogen by itself does nothing to provide a new source of energy.

Hydrogen does provide a number of viable alternatives as far as fuel production and distribution to consumers. It can be produced near an electric or chemical plant, bottled and shipped, or it can be produced locally at a gas station. In Japan and the United States, energy systems for homes that produce hydrogen from natural gas also are being suggested by industry leaders.[1]

However, in all the above technologies, hydrogen must be extracted from some other source and produced elsewhere in a liquid or gas form.

Each of these processes takes a significant amount of energy from some *other* energy source to create the hydrogen; hence, there is no net energy gain, only conversion of energy from one stored energy to another. In fact, energy is lost because of conversion inefficiencies.

Efficiency is an important criterion in determining energy alternatives. Energy efficiency considerations must include the entire "well to wheels" energy efficiency fuel chain. With oil, this efficiency includes pumping the oil from the well, refining gasoline and diesel, trucking the fuel to filling stations and turning the wheels of your car when it burns in an internal combustion engine. This total process is the fuel chain efficiency, or "well to wheels" efficiency.

Hydrogen, as an alternative fuel source to gasoline or coal, fares little better at "well to wheels" efficiency. In fact, Dr. Michael Wang, an energy scientist at the U.S. Department of Energy's Argone National Laboratories, recently reported the following in *Scientific American*:

> If you look at it from the whole system, not the individual sector, you may do no better to get rid of your coal-fired power plants, because coal is such a carbon-intensive fuel.[2]

Here, Wang alluded to the fact that hydrogen can be produced only by other energy sources. The U.S. grid, for example, relies on coal for 51.56 percent of its power.[3]

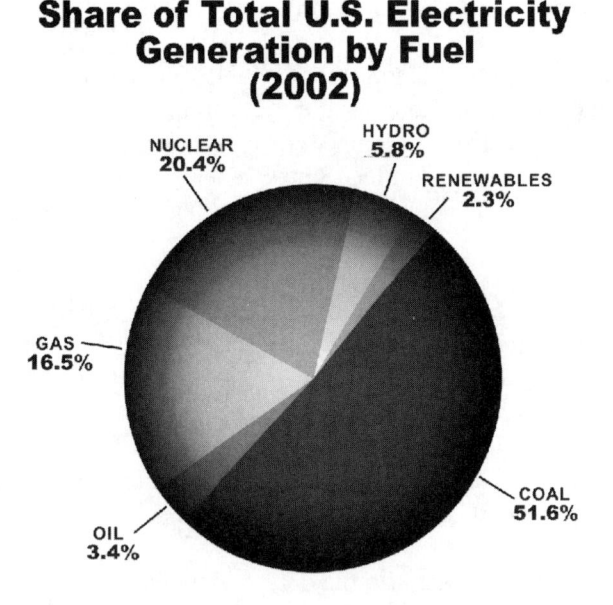

Figure 1-10. U.S. Electricity Generation by Fuel

The term "Hydrogen Economy," as it is predominantly used in the year 2004, is at best a growth path to other, better forms of energy. A complete solution, it isn't. Its greatest economic benefit will be to the existing nuclear power industry.

Nuclear power plants run at maximum efficiency when they run at full bore. However, consumers do not demand peak power throughout each 24-hour period. Hence, hydrogen production, through the surplus electrical power generated during low-demand periods of nuclear reactors, can be applied cost-effectively to the electrolytic production of hydrogen gas, reducing the fossil fuel contribution to the fuel chain and helping to reduce air pollution. As long as the nuclear fission plants run safely, this is a benefit to both the energy supply and the environment.

On a very small scale, wind power farms are excellent generators of hydrogen gas. Wind power, like nuclear power, may be present during times when consumer demand is low. The storage of energy from wind power through produced hydrogen is an effective energy storage solution in this case. As well, the storing of generated hydrogen for later transport to consumers can mitigate the problem of power transmission loss that occurs when wind farms are located at great distances from consumers.

An advantage of hydrogen is that it provides for cleaner energy *end use,* that is, vehicle emissions of greenhouse gases, at the point of consumption. Once burned, it produces only water as a byproduct. Generating hydrogen at the power plant (fossil fuel or nuclear) would allow the associated pollution or reactor safety issues to be located away from populated rural areas and cities.

A disadvantage is that hydrogen is not nearly as energy-dense as gasoline in energy content per cubic centimeter, and the storage space required for the equivalent amount of hydrogen that will offer the same energy density as gasoline is much larger. This presents a significant engineering problem for fuel economy. One avenue toward resolving the energy-density issue is a research effort under way to pressurize or store it in solid form.

While certain legislators happily announce plans for a "Hydrogen Economy" in their state, what they really are doing, in essence, is a NIMBY (Not In My Back Yard) switch: shifting the pollution (in the case of coal) or danger (in the case of nuclear fission) to another state, where the hydrogen is being produced!

Needless to say, the combustion of hydrogen itself, as a chemical fuel, does nothing to help with the problem of peak oil or national energy independence. Nor does it provide a pathway to a pollution-free and radiation-free sustainable energy future. Only fusion of hydrogen nuclei, releasing 8 million times that of the chemical use of hydrogen, will bring about a true "Hydrogen Economy," with energy payoffs for generations ahead.

CHAPTER SEVEN

The Distant Promise of Exotic New Energies

Nanotechnology Energy Alternatives

Nanotechnology, or nano science, is a new addition to the world of energy alternatives. Nanotechnology is the study of matter at atomic scales, that is, several billionths of a meter or less. The concepts in nanotechnology were started by Nobel laureate Richard Feynman in a famous talk, "There is Plenty of Room at the Bottom," given on Dec. 29, 1959. Feynman suggested the idea of studying extremely small things, down to atomic and molecular levels of smallness.[1]

Forty years later, nanotechnology finally has been funded within the National Nanotechnology Initiative by the U.S. Congress on a year-to-year basis. The science of nanotechnology cuts across many scientific disciplines, from physics and electronics to biology and chemistry. Commercial applications for nanotechnology include everyday consumer electronics, such as liquid crystal flat-screen display televisions, and clothing that is highly water-repellent.

Nobel laureate Richard Smalley, of Rice University, in Houston, Texas, explained why nanotechnology is important to energy. Smalley has been pounding the pavement the last few years with ideas to help the nanotechnology industry. He recently commented:

I think nanotech will play a role in providing the answers to these seemingly impossible problems that we all agree are soon going to be our children's problems. My idea is that, if you solve the energy question, you'll solve a lot of those other problems in the process.[2]

Nanotechnology's recent assistance to the energy industry includes better fuel cells and even flexible solar nanomaterials that can be dispensed on rolls of plastic tape like a ribbon. Smalley was quoted in the *MIT Technology Review*:

The fabulous notion here is that we may be able to put this active agent in some spreadable medium and basically print these things.[3]

The article said that, in fact, if this nanomaterial can just collect a mere fraction of the trillions of watts of solar energy the earth receives from the sun every year, it could trickle-charge batteries on small electronics such as cell phones and maybe even provide surplus power for homes and cars. This would help to decrease our dependence on fossil fuels in the process.

Interestingly, much of the work in cold fusion research seems to be heading in this direction. The same kinds of nanoequipment used to study atoms and molecules in the nanotechnology field might be used to help study key aspects of the materials science in cold fusion research, as well.

Zero-Point Energy

For those willing to venture into the outer fringes of energy research, the concept of zero-point energy is discussed with great zeal in Internet discussion lists and periodic regional conferences. Proponents consider zero-point energy to be a technology able to tap a source of energy that exists all around us in free space. Some refer to this as "space energy" or "vacuum energy," and they believe that its potential is enormous. Most conventional scientists have rather unflattering and highly cynical words for this subject.

Regardless, one researcher, quoted in *Aviation Week & Space Technology*, stated, "The potential is practically limitless, way beyond what can be conceived." He added that engineering challenges are impeding research progress, so experiments so far "have produced about the same amount of energy as a butterfly's wing - picowatts or so. But the potential is there." [4]

While the idea appears to have strong support from a few highly qualified scientists, many researchers in the field of zero point energy do not tend to adhere to certain aspects of the scientific process.

For example, their work appears to be driven mainly by inventors and speculative investors. Access to specific details is generally limited to those who sign nondisclosure agreements or arrange investment agreements. This tends to prevent nearly everyone else, including academics and the press, from evaluating work in the field.

If the claims of zero-point energy promoters are indeed fulfilled by the delivery of their products rather than by scientific validation, the marketplace, rather than scientists, will attest to the veracity of such novel devices. Mark Goldes, chairman and chief executive officer of Magnetic Power Inc., wrote in June, 2004, "I believe we are close to being able to license products for the market. I believe customers will be the ultimate judges." Goldes wrote, "Once the technology is in the marketplace, academics in several countries will undoubtedly become deeply involved." [5]

Jed Rothwell, webmaster for the www.lenr-canr.org cold fusion library, has followed the claims of zero-point energy for many years. Rothwell doesn't believe them. He said, "[Zero-point energy experiments] have not been made fully public, and they have not been replicated. No one should believe such claims. Any claim, conventional or radical, must be published and replicated."

Rothwell further critiqued the way in which the zero-point energy field has differed from cold fusion and other fields of science:

> The scientific method demands replication, and it demands that published papers be made freely available to all readers, so that people everywhere can evaluate the results and root out mistakes. Every detail must be revealed and peer-reviewed. This is fundamental. Without these rules, you have chaos. [6]

One interested observer, Steven Johnson, discussed his hopes that zero-point energy will deliver as its proponents promise:

> I have a tremendous desire to want to believe. I want to believe that the theory of zero-point energy, like those reported by Mr. Goldes, will soon become a reality. Who wouldn't! But believing, I've learned, is a double-edge sword. Believing has sustained me through dark times when nobody else believed what I believed was possible. However, believing in something, I realized, when not backed with reproducible evidence, really should be called a faith.[7]

Rothwell shared his strong viewpoints on the distinction between faith and science:

> Faith is the enemy of science. They can never co-exist. A scientist may have faith in God, or the human spirit, or the Boston Red Sox, but they must leave that part of their personality outside the laboratory door if they hope to succeed. Faith is normal, and healthy, and good for people, but not in this job - not during business hours.
>
> It is a little like being a soldier. Soldiers may be loving fathers or mothers and fine human beings in regular life, but when they go to work on the battlefield, they must put that aside and kill people in cold blood. Regrets or hesitation would be fatal. To be a soldier or scientist, [on the job] you must deny a large part of what makes us human. That is why these jobs are not popular and why few people make good scientists.

Storms, an expert in cold fusion, sees something intrinsically hopeful about the zero-point energy concept. He said, "Even if cold fusion does prove to be a viable source of energy, it's not going to be the only novel alternative. In theory, zero-point energy is far more infinite in its capacity and in its convenience [for useful application]."

Storms also offered an interesting long-range perspective: "I view cold fusion as a transition between our current situation and another energy source. In the long run, zero-point energy will most likely be the most effective source of energy." [8]

For now, however, Storms directs his enthusiasm toward cold fusion research. He eagerly awaits the results promised by the zero-point energy advocates, but he suspects that they have a much longer road ahead of them than they themselves anticipate.

Sonofusion and Bubble Fusion

"Bubble Fusion" caused quite a stir in March 2002, when a team of researchers led by Rusi Taleyarkhan of the U.S. Oak Ridge National Laboratory startled the world with, essentially, a miniature form of hot fusion. Significant evidence exists that this technique is another form of inertial confinement fusion. Its formal name is acoustic inertially confined fusion.

An unusual and little-understood phenomenon associated with bubble fusion is that, during the process, ultrasonic waves used to generate the bubbles also create discharges of light through an effect that is referred to as sonoluminescence. Although scientists have known for some time that sonoluminescence can occur when ultrasound is used to create bubbles, before the Taleyarkhan work, they did not know that it might be possible to produce fusion reactions with this method.

Using a solution of acetone and deuterium, Taleyarkhan's team bombarded the cell with acoustic (ultrasonic) waves and neutron irradiation, creating a new means to spark a hot fusion fire from nanometer-sized bubbles.[9]

In spite of this, Dr. Scott Chubb perceives Sonofusion to be closer to cold fusion. Chubb is a theoretical physicist who has worked on cold fusion as a consultant for Research Systems Corporation for more than a decade, while also being employed for the last 15 years (in areas other than cold fusion) by the U.S. Naval Research Laboratory. He explained key areas of distinction between bubble fusion and sonofusion in a somewhat technical, but thorough, science lesson:

> Believe it or not, more than one form of bubble fusion exists, and this has caused a degree of confusion. In particular, the bubble fusion developed at Oak Ridge involves a phenomenon referred to as acoustic cavitation, which has also been used by Roger Stringham.

In both situations, sound waves create unstable forms of bubbles that implode, with extremely high pressure and velocity. Some people also suggest the bubbles achieve high temperature; but the implosion occurs so rapidly that the concept of temperature is not well-defined.

An important source of confusion has been that, although superficially, since both the Stringham and Oak Ridge procedures involve acoustic cavitation, at least initially, people tended to refer to both sets of results interchangeably, using the term sonofusion.

In fact, Stringham and [former associate Russ] George invented the term sonofusion, in order to distinguish their work from the Fleischmann-Pons type of cold fusion. Their experiments should be referred to as sonofusion, while the Oak Ridge experiments should be referred to as bubble fusion.[10]

Stringham discussed his many years of experience working with acoustic cavitation before his work with sonofusion:

In March of 1989, when Fleischmann and Pons announced their work, I was using the cavitation bubble as a unique research tool. I also had in the laboratory heavy water and palladium foils and piezo-driven reactors. Within a day, I was able to see that the cavitation energy produced excess heat. It seemed to me that cavitation was just as viable as the electrochemical method used by Fleischmann and Pons. My first experiments were clumsy but intriguing. Particularly evident was the condition of the palladium foil after exposure to cavitating heavy water. The metal target had melted spots (greater than 1,800 degrees Celsius) and was discolored. I was hooked.[11]

Chubb further explained the difference between sonofusion and bubble fusion:

The distinguishing feature of the Stringham (sonofusion) work is that, when the bubbles implode, they strike a metal target, while in the Oak Ridge (bubble fusion) effort, the bubbles implode upon themselves. This distinction is important because, in the presence of the metal (typically palladium), as in the sonofusion (cold fusion) case, helium-4 and tritium are produced without high energy byproducts, while in the Oak Ridge experiments, where the bubbles implode on themselves, tritium and neutrons are produced, in a manner that is more reminiscent of conventional fusion. But even in the Oak Ridge situation, the reaction does not completely mimic conventional fusion. The amounts of tritium and neutrons are very different, and this has resulted in a degree of controversy.

Storms clarified another distinction between the two:

> The nuclear reactions produced by the Stringham method occur within the palladium metal, while the bubble fusion generates the nuclear reactions within a plasma generated by the bubble. In the case of Stringham's method, the bubble is used only as another [of the many] methods to inject deuterium into the [palladium] metal.[12]

To summarize the configuration differences, the sonofusion acoustic cavitation experiments use ultrasonic waves as the catalyst, and the reaction occurs in the presence of a metal (palladium) and a form of water (D_2O,) similar to cold fusion. Bubble fusion experiments use ultrasonic waves and neutron bombardment as the catalyst, but the reaction occurs in the presence of acetone, a highly flammable material, and appears to be a form of hot fusion.

In terms of potential, Stringham commented:

> This is a robust method of producing excess energy several times that of the input. At this point, our work and technology is at the door of being a practical device as a power-mutiplier as in a water heater device.[13]

Russian Academy of Sciences physicist Andrei Lipson notes that his team performed work with acoustic cavitation as early as 1990, though Taleyarkhan apparently failed to cite his earlier paper published in *Soviet Technical Physics Letters,* as well as the translation in the American Institute of Physics journal *Technical Physics Letters.* Lipson's team measured neutron emissions, which provided clear evidence of a nuclear reaction in these types of experiments. He said that the Oak Ridge work is a long way from commercialization:[14]

The energy produced in bubble fusion is many orders of magnitude less than that necessary to create the effect. So, even if bubble fusion really exists, it will have much longer to get to a practical application than compared with electrochemical cold fusion.[15]

Storms pointed out an unavoidable logistical problem with bubble fusion:

This kind of fusion has been worked on at many laboratories, including Los Alamos. However, only Oak Ridge solved the critical problem of achieving sufficient temperature in the bubble. Unfortunately, the fusion rate is trivial. If they produced one watt of thermal power, the neutron flux would quickly destroy the acetone. So you see, this is not a practical method to produce fusion power.[16]

Comparing the energy options available to humankind, both those available and those that are a glimmer of hope in scientists' minds, cold fusion fares well. Before we review the experimental evidence for cold fusion (in Part Three), Part Two will explore the awkward and difficult birth of this new field of energy research.

Part Two

A HISTORICAL PERSPECTIVE

CHAPTER EIGHT

An Overdue Revolution in Science

Fifteen years after the initial announcement of cold fusion, evidence for this new science is extraordinary, and an impressive array of scientists now strongly asserts that cold fusion is *real*. While theoretical understanding remains incomplete, scientists' capacity to replicate and demonstrate the revolutionary heat-generating effect has matured dramatically. Virtually all points of initial criticism have been answered.

During these past 15 years, scientists around the world repeatedly, through a variety of methods, have found evidence that shows cold fusion is indeed a nuclear process. A new, previously unknown source of energy in the form of excess heat has been measured convincingly with precise calorimeters. Nuclear products have been found in significant quantities. And, most important, the quantities of energy released and their commensurate nuclear products match closely, in agreement with Einstein's theory of relativity, $E=mc^2$, and as required by the law of conservation of mass-energy.

Sandia National Laboratories is one of the United States' most important government-owned sites for the development of science-based technologies that support national security. In September 2003, James Corey, a senior member of the technical staff at Sandia, delivered to the 2003 Energetic Materials Intelligence Symposium a presentation titled "History of and Current Claims for [Cold Fusion]." The presentation summarized the evidence in support of and the imminent issues pertaining to the field.

Corey identified various economic and national security concerns related to potential changes in energy production and world trade.[1] He noted that several countries surpass the United States in their level of support for cold fusion research and development. In particular, China, which has extensive ornamental plating manufacturing facilities, readily could take the lead in commercializing a new method of cold fusion known as "thin film low energy nuclear reactions."

Although not mentioned in Corey's presentation, Japan also has demonstrated a strong commitment to cold fusion research. Japan's Mitsubishi Heavy Industries is known to have a multiyear program in cold fusion experimentation. Toyota, Canon and Honda are rumored to be engaged in cold fusion research.[2] And Akito Takahashi, retired from Osaka University, reports that, in a few cases, cold fusion is taught at the graduate level in Japanese universities.[3]

In Corey's presentation, he predicted the following:

> An overdue revolution in science will arrive, [and] the reputations of cold fusion scientists, and those who revile them, may be reversed.[4]

Although prominent science journals have been loath to acknowledge the growing mountain of evidence, and unanswered questions remain, hundreds of world-class scientists, including more than 60 physicists,[5] most with extensive previous experience in hot fusion, have come to accept the reality of cold fusion.

Dr. George Miley, director of the Fusion Studies Laboratory at the University of Illinois, Urbana, 1995 recipient of the Edward Teller Medal from the American Nuclear Society, and past editor of its Fusion Technology journal for 15 years, summarized the status of cold fusion science in a November 2003 e-mail:

> Experimental evidence has now verified that nuclear reactions can be caused to occur in heavily loaded solids [that is, palladium]. It is premature to predict where this is headed from an applications point of view, but the basic science is clearly revolutionary.[6]

The Old Versus the New Fusion

Historically, the greatest opposition to any new scientific field has come from those invested in established approaches - in this case, the hot fusion industry and its academic grant recipients. Obviously, they have more at stake than others, because funding increases for cold fusion likely would mean decreases for hot fusion. Hence their skepticism of newcomers offering claims that defy the prevailing scientific paradigm. Hot fusion's proponents are also the ones in the seat of authority, and their voices give sway to public opinion. For 15 years, they have persuaded the scientific establishment to ignore, suppress and, at times, censor new findings and discoveries that corroborated the Fleischmann-Pons discovery.

Cold fusion's most vocal opponents, the conventional fusion experts who have vested interests in the status quo, have created such a mythology around cold fusion that it has ubiquitously and erroneously become known as the greatest scientific mistake of the century. Cold fusion has come to symbolize the epitome of something unattainably idealistic, or of a crazy idea, or the impossible dream.

The new fusion was proposed to occur not in the old three-story, billion-dollar behemoths in which the old fusion, concomitant with its deadly neutron emissions and gamma radiation, took place (Figure 2-1) but in a small test tube, devoid of lethal radiation, for less than $100,000.

Figure 2-1. Tokamak Fusion Test Reactor at the Princeton Plasma Physics Lab, USA. This test reactor generated only 27 percent of its input power at its peak.
(Image Courtesy of Princeton Plasma Physics Lab)

If this doesn't work we're going to look pretty silly.

Figure 2-2. Cold Fusion Frustrations, by Joan Cartier

Soon after the Fleischmann-Pons announcement, thousands of scientists worldwide worked feverishly around the clock to replicate the cold fusion experiment. Within a few months, most gave up in defeat. Chemists and related researchers seemed to achieve a better rate of success than others. Dr. Edmund Storms, at the time a radiochemist working for Los Alamos National Laboratory, had better luck than most.

Storms recalled the excitement of cold fusion research in the days immediately following the Fleischmann-Pons discovery:

> In 1989 at Los Alamos, the lab almost came to a standstill because so many people took time off from their regular tasks to study cold fusion. Hundreds of people were working on the cold fusion project. The auditorium would be packed with individuals who were interested in learning about the subject or doing experiments. The director of the laboratory at the time remarked, "This is absolutely amazing. Physicists and chemists are actually talking to each other. This hasn't happened since the war years!" This approach was occurring in many nations all over the world. Experiments were being done everywhere. Unfortunately, very few of these succeeded. Three groups succeeded at Los Alamos, and I was in one of them.[7]

Seeing the result for himself opened Storms' mind to the possibility of a reality that could support such a phenomenon. He is now a top cold fusion instructor and experimentalist and a prolific author of cold fusion papers, including several comprehensive surveys of the field. One of his most popular works, "A Student's Guide to Cold Fusion," is available at www.lenr-canr.org. Storms' own Web site, www.edstorms.com, is an excellent resource for students and pros alike.

Storms met his wife, Carol Talcott, when they worked together at Los Alamos on cold fusion experiments - and found that they had good chemistry together. After his retirement from Los Alamos, they moved to nearby Santa Fe, where they built and designed a house and separate cold fusion laboratory/art studio where they could pursue their individual passions.

Storms' laboratory is small, but packed with a wide variety of equipment that reflects the breadth of his skills. To perform his ground-breaking research in this entirely new field, in addition to the standard electrochemical apparatus, Storms uses laser equipment, a high vacuum turbo-molecular pump, an electronics bench, a custom glass-blowing setup, a miniature metal shop and a host of instrumentation and data acquisition devices coupled to several of his computers. He has spent $100,000 of his own retirement savings to equip the lab and pay for raw materials.

Figure 2-3. Dr. Edmund Storms
(Photo by Steven Krivit)

The white-bearded Storms exudes knowledge and wisdom, serenity, patience, compassion and humor. He joked, "Being nearly 6½ feet tall and living at 8,300 feet gives me a really good view of the world." His unusual physical vantage point echoes his unique philosophical views on science and humanity. One of several insightful commentaries he has written is titled, "When Will We Learn to Listen?" The following is an excerpt:

Suppose a discovery were made that would eliminate many serious problems of modern times. Global warming could be reduced, air pollution in major cities could be eliminated, and energy for heating and transportation would become cheap and readily available. Cutting of the rain forest and lack of water in desert regions would become problems of the past. Food would become plentiful, as cheap water became available from the sea. Even if these claims turn out to be exaggerated, I'm sure you would welcome such information and breathe a sigh of relief with us all. This would seem like a gift from God designed to protect us from our present lack of restraint in destroying our planet.

Now suppose such a discovery has been made but is rejected by the general scientific profession because it does not fit present understanding, by major governments because of their typical lack of imagination and by major industries because of feared competition. So many examples exist of new ideas being rejected for these reasons that this story would seem to be rather commonplace and unimportant.

Let us further suppose that a few governments did recognize the importance of the discovery and began supporting work to understand and develop its potential. No one would be surprised if such countries were Japan, China and India. Each, unlike the West, has a great need to solve such problems by finding sources of cheap energy. In the process of developing this discovery, these countries would discover some very interesting consequences. They would find that cars could be powered using water rather than gasoline. Immediately, all present car designs would become obsolete, and car production in the West would plummet. Engines of such high power and efficiency could be created to make international travel cheap and fast. Consequently, present airplane design would become obsolete. Each new technological application would have to be purchased from one of these inventive countries. As a result, the West would go into economic decline. Now the story is beginning to sound like a B-rated science-fiction movie.

Unfortunately, most of what I have described is real and is happening. Like all great discoveries of the past, this one also is hidden from all but a few people. However, because of the overwhelming importance of this discovery and the short time we have to solve some of the serious world-problems, a few knowledgeable people are trying to make the information more available to the general public. If the consequences were not so important, we would wait until reality forced recognition by even the most slow-witted bureaucrat and the most self-righteous scientist. In this case, we do not have the time to wait.[8]

CHAPTER NINE

The Moment of Discovery

Drs. Martin Fleischmann and Stanley Pons, the inventors of "cold fusion," did not begin their illustrious-turned-infamous careers with the intention to bring into the world a new energy source that might revolutionize the planet. Contrary to many popular accounts, they were neither opportunists seeking fame and glory nor "mad scientists" interested to defy the laws of physics.

Martin Fleischmann

Many regard Fleischmann as one of the world's top electrochemists. While he is best known for co-discovering cold fusion, he was first a leader in many aspects of electrochemistry, the science behind battery research. If one single quality describes Fleischmann, it is his driving passion for discovery. Fleischmann has been known for breaking ground that other scientists have followed to great commercial success. Cold fusion, he said in a 2003 interview, was only one of the interesting projects he and Pons were working on in 1989. To his great dismay, academia's hostile response to cold fusion caused such damage to his reputation that he was unable to remain in academia or continue to challenge his mind with these other creative projects.

Fleischmann was born on March 29, 1927, in Czechoslovakia. His mother was a Roman Catholic. "There is a considerable mystery about my paternal grandfather," Fleischmann wrote. "I have heard him described both as a Slovak and a Hungarian. There is no doubt that he came from Banska Štiavnica in Slovakia (or its environs) and that he was an orphan. He was adopted by a Jewish family called Fleischmann; his first name was Maximillian." [1]

When Fleischmann was a boy, he and his family got caught up in the Nazi occupation of Western Czechoslovakia in 1938 but managed to escape - twice. Christopher Tinsley of *Infinite Energy* magazine spoke with Fleischmann in detail about these personal experiences:

> I always tell people I had the unique and unpleasurable experience of being arrested by the Gestapo at the age of 11. These things tend to concentrate your mind somewhat, you know, and my father was very badly beaten up by the Nazis. However, we got out.

> We were driven across the border by a First World War comrade-in-arms of my father. He was a fighter pilot in the Austrian Army, and my father was an artillery officer, and they were very close friends. They were big heroes locally. He drove us across; he had a taxi firm. He himself drove us across into the unoccupied part of Czechoslovakia. That was the first time we got away.

> The second time, [after the Nazi occupation expanded], it wasn't clear where we [would go]. We might have gone to Canada or Argentina - or South Wales, actually. But we couldn't get any money out [of the bank]. My parents were going to start a factory in South Wales, but this couldn't be arranged, and we lost everything. In the end, my sister was adopted by a Methodist minister and his wife in Cheadle Hulme. The wife's brother lived in Llandudno, and she told him that he had to adopt me, which he did. He was a bachelor, and he adopted me. I find this very difficult to talk about. I must say, when Gene [Mallove] asked me about it, I burst into tears, which I am prone to do when I recall this ancient history.

> At the time [of our second escape], my parents had received permission to come to England. We all got on the train in Prague and came to the Dutch border. Then the Germans cleared the train of all refugees. We were in the last coach, and my father said, "No, sit tight, don't get off the train," and [moments later] the train pulled out of the station. So that's how we got away the second time, and

arrived at Liverpool Street Station with 27 shillings and sixpence between the four of us.[2]

Several years later, Fleischmann passed the University of London's Imperial College entrance examination and obtained an entrance scholarship. His studies were concerned with platinum and hydrogen, but he developed an interest in palladium and hydrogen. In 1948, he began his doctoral program at the college, and two years later he earned his doctorate in chemistry. One of his instructors, who noted his tremendous talent for innovation, described Fleischmann as a "brilliant contributor with an oft-demonstrated flair for new ideas." [3]

He met his future wife, Sheila Flinn, in 1947 and married her after his graduation from the Ph.D. program. They had one son and two daughters; as of 2004, he is the proud grandfather of eight. Fleischmann went on to teach at Durham University in the United Kingdom. He brought considerable experimental innovation not only to the school but also to the field of electrochemistry.

In 1967, at the remarkably young age of 40, Fleischmann was offered a position as the chair of electrochemistry at the University of Southampton. There, he built up the department and, in doing so, earned it a world-class reputation. He was the recipient of numerous awards during this time. From 1970 to 1972, he held the prestigious post of president of the International Society of Electrochemists. In 1979, he was awarded the medal for electrochemistry and thermodynamics by the Royal Society of London. In 1983, he retired from Southampton. Two years later, in 1985, he was awarded the Palladium Medal by the U.S. Electrochemical Society, and he received the highest honor for an English scientist, Fellowship in the Royal Society.

Although officially retired, Fleischmann continued to pursue his research interests, at times with scientists at the United Kingdom's Harwell Atomic Energy laboratory and at times with his colleague and friend Pons at the University of Utah. Gene Mallove wrote fondly of Fleischmann in his book, *Fire from Ice: Searching for the Truth Behind the Cold Fusion Furor:*

> Fleischmann has been called a genuine Renaissance man with a reputation for brilliant and creative ideas - not all of which pan out,

but such is the nature of creativity. Surely, when one listens to or is in the presence of Martin Fleischmann, one feels that the image of an exceptional polymath fits him like a glove.[4]

B. Stanley Pons

Pons has remained outside of the public view for the last half-decade. An independently wealthy member of a family in the textile business, he had the rare opportunity to pursue whatever professional opportunity he might choose. He grew up in Valdese, a small town in North Carolina. The town was started by a religious sect called the Waldenses, pre-Reformation Christians from Northern Italy and southeastern France. Pons, a member of the sect, now lives in southern France.

His childhood interest in chemistry became the driving force in his life. After 10 years in his family's business, Pons felt unfulfilled and missed the challenges of academic pursuits that he had begun as a Ph.D. student with Professor Harry Mark at the University of Michigan in 1965. He had abandoned that pursuit for personal reasons in 1967 (only a few months before he was to receive his Ph.D.). Mark alerted Pons to the fact that Southampton University was one of the top schools in the world for electrochemistry. After some introductions by Mark on behalf of Pons, he was admitted to the graduate program there in 1976. Pons met Fleischmann for the first time on his arrival in England. Because Pons wanted to remain in the particular field of electrochemistry that he had begun at Michigan (spectro-electrochemistry), Fleischmann recommended that he join the research group of Professor Alan Bewick, who was very active in that research area.

Once awarded his Ph.D., Pons held several academic posts before ending up in 1983 at the University of Utah, where in 1988 he became head of the chemistry department. Pons has published widely in the academic literature, having written or co-written more than 200 scientific papers.[5]

Fleischmann shared with Pons not only a fascination with electrochemistry but also the joys of culinary experimentation. They were known for creating marvelous feasts in the kitchen of Pons' home when Fleischmann came to visit. They also enjoyed skiing and hiking in the Utah mountains, and it was out of this cordial relationship one day on a hike up Utah's Mill Creek Canyon that the two began asking the "what if" questions that eventually led to their world-famous discovery.

Figure 2-4.   Figure 2-5.
Dr. Martin Fleischmann, 1989   Dr. Stanley Pons, 1989
(Photos Courtesy of J. Willard Marriott Library, University of Utah)

The Moment of Discovery

As far back as 1947, Fleischmann began thinking about what might happen with deuterium in the presence of palladium.

He and Pons noted in the 1989 announcement of their discovery that "the strange behavior of electrogenerated hydrogen dissolved palladium has been studied for well over 100 years." Scientists knew that palladium had the ability to absorb large quantities of hydrogen, or its isotope deuterium, and that very high pressures of hydrogen can be produced at the palladium surface by the electrochemical overpotential. Fleischmann and Pons also knew that helium had been reported to come from such experiments, which implied a nuclear reaction.

Two German experimenters, Dr. Fritz Paneth and Dr. Kurt Peters, had experimented with hydrogen in palladium as early as 1926, but they eventually gave up, thinking that their observations were the result of experimental error. It was another German, Alfred Cöhn, a physics professor at the University at Göttingen, whose 1929 paper first drew Fleischmann's attention.

A defining moment of discovery came to Fleischmann and Pons rather unexpectedly in early 1985. After running one palladium-deuterium electrolytic experiment for many weeks and seeing absolutely nothing, they increased the input current to the cell from 0.75 amperes to 1.5 amperes. At the end of the day, all seemed normal, and they went home for the night.

The next morning, however, quite a "problem" had occurred overnight.

Kevin Ashley, a graduate student in the Chemistry Department, was walking past the room on the way to his own classroom that morning when he noticed a commotion in the Pons laboratory. Out of curiosity, he wandered in. At the time, Ashley reported, he had no idea what sort of experiments Fleischmann and Pons had been working on:

> "It was strange. I came in in the morning, and there was a huge mess in the lab. Pons and Fleischmann had these strange smirks on their faces, and I couldn't understand what they were so happy about when the experiment had obviously blown up overnight. They weren't exactly talking about it." [6]

Charles Beaudette interviewed Ashley in detail in his book Excess Heat & Why Cold Fusion Research Prevailed:

> Kevin Ashley ... was one of the first to witness Room 1113 in the Henry Eyring building at the University of Utah the next morning, "The lab was a mess and there was particulate dust in the air. On their lab bench were the remnants of an experiment. The bench was one of those black-top benches that was made of very, very hard

material. ... The experiment was near the middle [of the bench] where there was nothing underneath. I was astonished that there was a hole through the thing. The hole was about a foot in diameter. Under the hole was a pretty- good-sized pit in the concrete floor. It may have been as much as four inches deep."

Ashley noticed that, far from looking devastated at their destroyed experiment, "Stan and Martin had these looks on their faces as though they were the cat that had just swallowed the canary."

In an August 2003 interview, Fleischmann retrospectively expressed concern, not pride, over this event: "This was an experiment with a considerable flipside: it could have gone wrong under particular conditions."[7]

From that point onward, Fleischmann and Pons used much smaller pieces of palladium. In fact, they used thin foils and wires to prevent subsequent experiments from becoming unstable:

We took care not to get into that same ballpark. We tried to design it away, thinking that we would eventually return to design it back in. As we conducted further research, we took great pains to try and avoid it.[8]

Fleischmann and Pons continued their cold fusion research for several years afterward, trying to keep their work as quiet as possible, for they suspected the spectacle which would ensue once the word came out. By early 1989, having spent $100,000 of their own private funds, they reached their self-funding limit. According to Fleischmann, they also felt obliged to inform the U.S. Department of Energy of what they had discovered.

The Infamous Press Conference

Things got out of hand when University of Utah administrators, excited with fusion fever, geared up for fame and fortune.

Fleischmann and Pons had little choice in matters pertaining to the initial publicity and the infamous press conference. The University of Utah's patent- and grant-seeking interests took precedence over scientific protocol.

Fleischmann and Pons told the university that they would need many more months to complete a formal paper on the subject before making any announcement to the scientific community, but administrators wanted to announce the discovery before any paper had been published.

Fleischmann reflected on this stressful period of his life in an April 2004 letter: "I was not at all in favour of the high publicity route adopted by the University of Utah and wanted to delay consideration of publication until September 1990." But the university made it clear to him that he "had to appear supportive of their position." Fleischmann ran up against a wall with the university administration and attempted to use his prestigious connections to halt the press conference:

> I cast around for other means to put a spoke into the university's objectives. I tried to get hold of Lord Porter, the president of the Royal Society, to ask him to contact Mrs. Thatcher, to ask her to get hold of George Bush (senior) to block the proceedings. I failed in my manoeuverings![9]

Eventually, the two electrochemists agreed with the university administrators to submit an abbreviated paper called a "Preliminary Note."

The University of Utah administration received word that the Fleischmann and Pons paper, "Electrochemically Induced Nuclear Fusion of Deuterium," had been formally accepted for publication on March 22, 1989, in the *Journal of Electroanalytical Chemistry*. Arrangements for a press conference to announce this news to the world were made sometime between March 20 and March 22. The press conference, not surprisingly, was a hastily and poorly planned affair.

The rushed announcement has been attributed to several factors. First and foremost was the university's objective to secure first place in the cold fusion race and to corner the market on the cold fusion intellectual property. A few miles away, at nearby Brigham Young University, physicist Steve Jones was working on another type of cold fusion experiment. It is now known that Jones' cold fusion was markedly different from Fleischmann and Pons': Jones' work showed no signs of being an energy-producing device. But this distinction was poorly understood by university administrators. On hearing rumors that Jones may be poised to announce "cold fusion," the University of

Utah moved to secure its place at the patent office by publicly announcing its "prior claim."

The press conference was a disappointment to many scientists who were eager to learn the details of the experiment. The press release announcing the March 23 conference, edited by university administrators, carefully limited the scientific details. Furthermore, and unfortunately, as author Charles Beaudette wrote, there were other communication problems:

> The Preliminary Note that was accepted for publication the previous day was not made available for distribution [at the press conference]. The omission constituted a breach of protocol, as did their failure to brief their colleagues in the chemistry and physics departments beforehand.[10]

It wasn't until 2½ weeks later, on April 10, that the paper was published in the *Journal of Electroanalytical Chemistry*.[11] Still, the preliminary note was devoid of many important details and highly inadequate as a guide for other scientists to replicate the experiment. It was clearly a hasty attempt on the university's part to establish a foothold for its patent objectives and, perhaps, its fame.

The university believed it had its hands on the most valuable patent in modern history, and for this reason it also prohibited Fleischmann and Pons from personally disclosing key details to their fellow scientists. Dr. Chase Peterson, the university president at the time, was forthright about the university's interest, as shown in written testimony to the U.S. Congress:

> Upon the advice of our patent counsel, it is not possible for the University of Utah to share research results with other laboratories, particularly national laboratories, until the information has been incorporated into a patent application and the application is on file in the patent office.[12]

This secrecy generated ill will not only among skeptics from around the world but also among academic peers at the University of Utah. Distrust, anger, and even rage mounted almost immediately when other scientists attempted to learn the essential details of the experiment so that they could, in earnest, prove or disprove the experiment, a normal part of the scientific process. But this was nearly an impossible task, considering the legal restrictions.

Some assert that Fleischmann and Pons never should have dared to use the word "fusion" until such time as they could fully provide the evidence to the nuclear physics community. The truth of the matter is that they were uncertain at the time. Originally, they titled their Preliminary Note "Electrochemically Induced Nuclear Fusion of Deuterium?" But editors who wanted the work to look more confident and, by association, make the university look better, deleted the question mark.

To add more fuel to the critics' fire, the chemists could not reproduce the cold fusion effect on demand. These circumstances provided mud for the outraged nuclear physicists and science journalists to sling at them.

Another factor that earned them disfavor was the fact that, in their Preliminary Note, Fleischmann and Pons offered data measuring neutron emissions. "But these measurements were quickly shown to be wrong,"[13] Storms noted. As a consequence, the nuclear physics community promptly raked them over the coals for the blunder.

While the official University of Utah press release and the Fleischmann-Pons efforts to measure nuclear products were rushed, the remainder of their work, the crucial aspects of their electrochemical experiment that really mattered, were not.

Their discovery, and subsequent announcement of a "hitherto unknown nuclear process" on March 23, 1989, was a natural extension of their creative exploration of the properties of materials commonly used in their field of expertise. Their specific configuration and methodology was unique, however, as were their results.

Unfortunately, Fleischmann and Pons were overly optimistic in their projections for the rate of scientific progress that would follow the discovery. They had greatly underestimated the backlash from academia.

One of the bold optimistic statements from the University of Utah press release attributed to them that they would surely live to regret read as follows:

Our indications are that the discovery will be relatively easy to make into a usable technology for generating heat and power, but continued work is needed, first, to further understand the science and, second, to determine its value to energy economics.

"Relatively easy," as it turns out, has been anything but, and initially caused nothing but resentment and frustration from other scientists who felt misled. John Bockris, an electrochemist retired from Texas A&M University, described his view of the public statements:

> There is another way in which Fleischmann and Pons were delinquent. There was nothing in the "McNeil/Lehrer Hour" [when the news was first broadcast around the world] about the fact that one had to wait hundreds of hours before the effect switched on. I know that they were conscious of this in the early days because I visited them in Salt Lake City a few weeks after the announcement, and I recall standing by an apparatus with Pons and his telling me that the current had been flowing for three months, and he intended to let it go on six months before he shut it off.[14]

It was not until December of 1989 that Fleischmann and Pons completed the full paper and submitted it to the *Journal of Electroanlytical Chemistry*. Another six months passed before the paper was published, in July 1990. What normal scientists would have been willing to wait that long to try their hand at this earth-shattering claim of room temperature fusion?

In retrospect, that *any* other scientist was able to replicate any aspect of the discovery is a wonder in itself. Some, like the California Institute of Technology (Caltcch) scientists, desperate for experimental parameters, resorted to measuring newspaper photographs to obtain what they (erroneously) thought were the proper dimensions of the cold fusion cell!

By the time the details were published in the formal paper, most scientists had given up. The media and the overwhelming interest from the scientific community had faded away. In their place remained disappointment and disgust at what many scientists who struggled to replicate the effect thought was just a big waste of time and money. Within half a year, the scientific community pronounced cold fusion a hoax and accused Fleischmann and Pons of practicing "pseudo-science."

Fleischmann looks back with sadness on these times. "I really didn't want to do it this way. I did not want to do this project this way," he said in an interview in 2003.[15]

When the situation in Utah became intolerable, Fleischmann and Pons accepted an offer from Minoru Toyoda, one of the founders of the Toyota Motor Company, to set up their own, brand new, multimillion-dollar laboratory in Provence, France, to continue their research. Fleischmann, who was retired with grown children, happily accepted the offer. He said, "It was exciting to make a move, and it was a relief to get away from that terrible atmosphere in the United States." The circumstances were painful for Pons' family, according to his wife, Sheila Pons:

> We had to leave. It was impossible to go on. My daughter was in school at the time. She was 11 or 12 years old. And the kids would ask her, "Why did your father do this to us? Why did he have Utah smeared like this?" So we had a choice of staying in America and not continuing - or leaving America and continuing on, and that was difficult.

Pons was clear about the decision at hand and the sacrifices he was willing to make in order to continue:

> The decision wasn't difficult for me. [But] it was difficult to convince my family that they had to leave to preserve science, or what one man believes in science. I am bitter that I had to make such a stupid choice, and yes, I would give up my U.S. citizenship.[16]

CHAPTER TEN

Con-Fusion

The answer to what brought Fleischmann and Pons ill repute lies in a combination of scientific and human factors that are integral to the acceptance or rejection of any radically new scientific endeavor: the competition for resources and acclaim, the personalities of the various scientists and officials involved, and the problems of communication that develop when conflicting scientific paradigms and interests are at hand. The simplest and most fundamental point of controversy was that the claims of nuclear energy, without harmful side effects, produced by a relatively inexpensive mechanism, sounded just too good to be true.

The phenomenon challenged everyone's expectations of what could be achieved through chemistry. Nuclear reactions from a chemistry experiment, such as the electrolytic process that Fleischmann and Pons used, were unheard of. Physics Professor Robert Bush of the California Polytechnic Institute, Pomona, an early cold fusion pioneer, recalls that the nuclear physics community almost immediately began expressing strong doubts about the unique presentation of the supposed nuclear reaction:

> The idea that two chemists could be doing this on a table top really sounded almost "Alice in Wonderlandish," I must say. So I think our reaction was not unlike that of other physicists who thought, on the one hand, "Gee, that would be marvelous if they're doing it," and on the other hand, "My God! - Chemists doing it for probably pennies compared to what physicists have taken from the public coffer over the last 40 years - on the order of billions of U.S. dollars to do hot fusion." So the nuclear physics community said, "Well, you know,

the nuclear physics of this is looking very strange. It doesn't seem to be right. Where are the neutrons? Where are the gamma rays?"

According to conventional fusion theory, neutrons or gamma rays should have killed the chemists if the experiments had generated as much power as they claimed:

> Eventually, I think because of this bad nuclear physics and because of the fact that people were having difficulty reproducing this, the physicists threw out the good "baby," which was the excess heat effect, along with the bad (nuclear interpretation) "bath water." That was very unfortunate.

> Physicists concluded that the nuclear interpretation was the result of "bad physics" being conducted by chemists who were theorizing outside of their field of expertise." [1]

Even if this were the case, Fleischmann and Pons were not *experimenting* outside of their field of expertise. This experiment could have been devised only by an electrochemist and, most likely, only by one who was a top expert in the field. It is highly unlikely this would have been discovered by anyone who had preconceived notions of an acceptable presentation for nuclear fusion. If an alternative approach to fusion were verifiably possible, physicists would have to reconsider major assumptions underlying traditional nuclear theory.

In David Goodstein's 1994 article "Whatever Happened to Cold Fusion," printed in the journal *Accountability in Research*, he wrote, "Scientists are aware that they must be prepared, from time to time, to be surprised by a phenomenon they previously thought to be impossible." Goodstein acknowledged that, in 1989, "the anti-cold fusion crowd was ... guilty" of failing to keep its scientific process "firmly rooted in experiment or observation, unladen with theoretical preconceptions." [2]

These scientists rushed in to pull the plug on cold fusion research rather than allowing experimentation to take its natural course, as scientific method would dictate. From this perspective, their outrage was political, not scientific. At the time, the U.S. Congress was considering diverting $25 million from the hot fusion budget for cold fusion research.

The hot fusion scientists' hostility provided fodder for much satire.

Figure 2-6. "The New Scientific Method"

Figure 2-7. "Boy Scouts" seek funding for cold fusion research. By Ben Marchant with help from Eric Frazer, Csiro & Dan Conlon

In a November 2002 interview on the University of Utah radio station KUER/PBS, Dr. Michael McKubre, the director of the Energy Research Center at SRI International, commented:

> 1989 was a particularly difficult time for the hot fusion community. They were under investigation. Questions were being asked why all the money had been spent and why so little progress had been made.

Funding was being cut. The last thing that community wanted was the suggestion that there's a much simpler and cheaper way to achieve the same result.[3]

McKubre is an electrochemist who has been involved in cold fusion since the beginning and who is recognized worldwide for his significant scientific contributions and leadership in the field. Beaudette provided an excellent biography in *Excess Heat & Why Cold Fusion Research Prevailed*:

Michael McKubre started his university education in Washington, D.C., when his father was with the New Zealand embassy. He went to high school there, and then for a couple of years to The George Washington University. He was back in New Zealand to complete his bachelor's degree, master's degree, and a Ph.D. in chemistry, geophysics and electrochemistry. As he explained it, "All during my Ph.D. studies, particularly in electrochemistry, scanning the literature and attending the conferences, it became clear that of all the places in the English-speaking world, the University of Southampton was the clear leader in electrochemical research." With considerable trepidation, he entered the graduate program in chemistry at Southhampton in 1977. Here was a boy from the sticks of New Zealand preparing to compete in the big arena.

The Department of Chemistry at Southampton was quite large. Its pre-eminence was due to the presence of two individuals. Graham Hills (later Sir Graham Hills) was McKubre's post-doctoral supervisor and mentor. Martin Fleischmann was the chief electrochemist there, and one of considerable global recognition. At that time, the department was considered the leading academic institution in Europe for electrochemistry.

McKubre was accepted in the graduate program and spent "a delightful two years .... two glorious years at Southampton learning a great deal about electrochemistry and the philosophy of science in the real world." From there, he went directly to SRI International, a private research institute in Menlo Park, California, where he has spent his working career.

A pattern begins to emerge for several of the top early players in this new field. Fleischmann, Pons, Bockris and McKubre each earned a doctoral degree in electrochemistry from the most respected European institution for that field of study. Each can be characterized as a brilliant, independent thinker, a leader in his field. Unlike physicists, who would have had to cross theoretical lines to engage in this research, these electrochemists were intimately familiar with the nature of the electrolytic experimental method, its design and instrumentation. This background gave these electrochemists a distinct advantage in early cold fusion research. Physicists and other chemists without these strengths were no match, and their frustration quickly turned to cynicism and ridicule.

CHAPTER ELEVEN

Ridicule and Violent Opposition

"When a new truth enters the world, the first stage of reaction to it is ridicule, the second stage is violent opposition, and in the third stage, that truth comes to be regarded as self-evident."

- The German philosopher Arthur Schopenhaurer (1788-1860)

Schopenhaurer's view of how we react to new paradigms has stood the test of time. Innovators often have been wrongly labeled as delusional, uninformed, fraudulent, and guilty of perpetrating a hoax. Why all of this reaction by a group of scientists - people pledged to be open-minded searchers of truth, who have been trained to draw conclusions very carefully, only after they examine the given evidence? New ideas can upset us, or "rattle our cage," in many ways. But this viciousness is self-defeating at a time when the world desperately needs new ideas, including and perhaps especially those ideas that sound crazy at first but that eventually may become self-evident.

When Fleischmann and Pons identified the anomalous energy reaction as "n-fusion" and as "an hitherto unknown nuclear process," they became easy targets for attack and eventual dismissal, primarily by nuclear physicists who evaluated their claims on the basis of conventional nuclear theory. Three laboratories - the California Institute of Technology (Caltech), the Massachusetts Institute of Technology (MIT) and the United Kingdom's Harwell Atomic Energy Research Laboratory - nearly immediately attempted to replicate Fleischmann and Pons' experiment.

Opinions vary as to whether the scientists at these laboratories attempted in earnest to replicate the claims. In MIT's case, the research team seems to have intended to bury them. Weeks before the final data analysis, the MIT Plasma Fusion Center held a party billed as a "Wake for Cold Fusion ... sponsored by *the Center for Contrived Fantasies*" (Figure 2-8) to mock the Utah scientists and their ideas.[1]

❦A WAKE FOR COLD FUSION **
(it's not over 'til it's over)

"Don't you remember? We were at Herb and Sally's, and Herb said he knew how to achieve fusion at room temperature, using only gin and vermouth."

❦ **PLACE** : NW16-213
❦ **DATE** : Monday, June 26
❦ **TIME** : 4 p.m.
❦ **DRESS** : black armbands optional

** *Sponsored by the Center for Contrived Fantasies*

Figure 2-8. MIT "Wake for Cold Fusion" Plasma Fusion Center Party Announcement

The character of the cold fusion debate further degraded into personal attack. One plasma fusion physicist who played a key role in the 1989 dismissal of cold fusion was Dr. William Happer, chairman of the Advisory Council of the Princeton Plasma Physics Laboratory, who said of Fleischmann and Pons, "just by looking at these guys on television, it was obvious that they were incompetent boobs."[2] One can only wonder what Happer would have said of Albert Einstein!

At the height of the cold fusion mayhem, or perhaps more accurately, at its low point, the annual meeting of the American Physical Society took place in Baltimore, Maryland, May 1-3, 1989. Historians regard Baltimore as the turning point in the general perception of cold fusion, in the eyes of both the public and academia. This shift came about in a shameful and unprofessional manner.

A witness to the crippling of the scientific process was Dorothy Browner Hubler, wife of a U.S. Navy scientist and member of the American Physical Society. Hubler is not a scientist but an educator. She has a double master's degree in education administration and counseling from John Hopkins, as well a third master's in French from Paris' famous Sorbonne University. She has traveled the world training teachers and in the process has developed a broad viewpoint of academia and of humanity in general. Her recollections on the Baltimore meetings are vivid, and her perspective is thought-provoking:

> I'm all for progress, and having taught in every phase in education, including training teachers all the way from elementary to university, I've seen many people disagree, in terms of one's rationale, philosophy, or even theory. But this [Baltimore meeting] really surprised me, because this was the first time that I had ever been at a professional meeting where people were, what I thought, well - very *uncivilized*.

> When discussing the probabilities of cold fusion, it's only natural, especially in the scientific world, that nothing is proven overnight. You have to research it, and those who are positive and even those who are negative need to just keep researching until you get evidence to prove or disprove one's theory.

But I was just appalled at the kind of verbal responses that were given. I did not expect to hear profanity; I did not expect to hear people calling other people names. I can understand an emotional reaction, but I thought this was just a little bit out of control.

I have been present at not only many scientific meetings but meetings in culture, economics and politics, due to my interests and profession as a retired educator. And having had this experience and attended conferences around the world, both with my husband and in my own personal career, I had never seen that kind of behavior displayed before - to the point of anger.

I'm all for disagreement, but you don't have to take it down in the gutter. We shouldn't attack people's character because we disagree with their thinking. When you are a scientist, you just don't get up and yell and scream and curse someone out.

You just don't turn [the scientists] away and say, "This is impossible." Nor do you try to crush the mind or the creativity of those who are trying to push forward in a particular area, such as cold fusion.

I have to say that those who were purporting the theory of cold fusion were extremely positive-minded and were very, very professional. And that gave me hope.

I remember saying to my husband, "You know, these kinds of things happen. Can you imagine when Einstein and his team came up with the atom bomb, or even the automobile, or the airplane with the Wright brothers? Can you image the dissent of the people [at that time]?" Progress sometimes is not well-received. The same thing [happened] with the discovery of DNA. It was not well received initially.

But at the same time, this is progress, you know. And these [types of breakthroughs] are what we expect of our scientists. They have to prove their hypothesis, and they have to research it. It's not the kind of thing that they go into blindly. They have to be creative, use their mind, and they need freedom to probe. This is how we got the space shuttle and all our space exploration. To me, this is the way progress and also inventions and technology came about. We had people who were determined that there was, in fact, something to their theories or formulas, and that brought about all kinds of progress. This is one of the things I have pride in about America; people tend to promote ideas, promote creativity.

Of course you're going to have your critics. It is only normal. But this was quite shocking to me. I, of course, maintained my composure, I just sat there. In fact, I almost wanted to cry. The reason was that I felt so sorry for the scientists who were delivering their papers. I thought it might take many years to prove, maybe 20, 25 years, but I believed in what they were doing because I think that all things are possible, and just because you don't prove it immediately doesn't mean that its not going to happen, especially with all the brilliant minds we have in science today, and with all the advanced apparatus and technology. I believe it's possible, and I think it will help the world, not just the U.S., but the whole world, for its energy needs and to help cut down the costs of energy. I think this is one of those research ideas that needs lots of support rather than lots of negativity.[3]

Chemist Nathan Lewis of Caltech was one of the scientists who claimed to have attempted to replicate the cold fusion effect. At this meeting, he announced that he saw "no evidence for any unusual nuclear or chemical reactions" in his lab.[4]

"Nathan was a violent opponent," Bockris wrote. "I have seen his face change color in fury at the suggestion that the effects may be real. I used to point out to him that 'one must not be an ostrich.'"[5]

Another Caltech scientist who made a mark for himself at Baltimore was Provost Steven Koonin. Speaking of the claims, he commented, "One could also theorize how pigs could fly if they had wings, but pigs don't have wings."[6]

In his concluding remarks, Koonin said, "We are suffering from the incompetence and perhaps delusions of Drs. Pons and Fleischmann."[7]

These personal assaults set a course for the two discoverers to be ousted from academia, and they provided a stern warning to all scientists who otherwise might consider the possibility that Fleischmann and Pons' claims were real.

Goodstein wrote:

> For all practical purposes, the cold fusion episode ended a mere five weeks after it began on May 1, 1989. All three scientists from Caltech [Steven Koonin, Nate Lewis, and Charlie Barnes, a physicist] executed between them a perfect slam-dunk that cast cold fusion right out of the arena of mainstream science.[8]

There is little disagreement over the disastrous consequences of the Caltech scientists' behavior. One reporter observed:

> Steve Koonin and Nate Lewis ... nearly killed cold fusion between them. Koonin later said that someone told him that he hit a triple and Lewis hit a home run. "He was good," Koonin said about Lewis. "People were just stunned." [9]

They were indeed stunned, Dorothy Hubler said. "It was just horrible," she remembered.[10]

Figure 2-9 "Harnessing Fusion Energy" The joke in the press at the time was that the only reliable way to harness fusion energy was to hook chemists and physicists to microphones and let them 'go at it.' Copyright, Tribune Media Services, Inc. All Rights Reserved.

CHAPTER TWELVE

A Biased 1989 Review Panel

In November 1989, eight months after the initial cold fusion announcement, a panel of individuals from industry and academia dealt a critical blow to cold fusion.

The cold fusion panel, under the auspices of the Energy Resources Advisory Board, was selected and directed by John Huizenga, Professor Emeritus of chemistry and physics at the University of Rochester, New York, a school with a prominent U.S. Department of Energy-funded hot fusion program. In Huizenga's 1993 book *Cold Fusion: The Scientific Fiasco of the Century*, he wrote, "My initial feeling was that the whole cold fusion episode would be short-lived and that it would be wise to delay appointing such a panel." [1]

The implications, as Huizenga later stated more directly, were that cold fusion was merely "pathological science" and that this would become evident shortly; hence, a panel would not be necessary.

With such an attitude by the panel's chairman, it is not surprising that the panel concluded that cold fusion should not receive special federal funding.

Most people did not understand that, while the panel members *rejected* cold fusion as a recipient for special funding, they never *disproved* it. Regardless, the sociological and political effect was the same.

Another important, little-known fact is that Nobel laureate Norman F. Ramsey, a Harvard University physics professor, served as panel co-chair. In desperation, he threatened to resign from the panel if it did not include the following preamble in the report:

> With the many contradictory existing claims, it is not possible at this time to state categorically that all the claims for cold fusion have been convincingly either proved or disproved, [but] even a single short but valid cold fusion period would be revolutionary.[2]

Not wanting to have to explain to the public why a Nobel physics laureate resigned from their panel, Huizenga and the others conceded. Ramsey alone demonstrated the vision and the courage to voice a dissenting opinion and to express the truth despite tremendous social and political pressure to do otherwise.

Other members of the panel were less courageous, even though some of them apparently agreed with Ramsey, as Dr. Tom Passell noted. Passell is one of the program managers for the Electric Power Research Institute (EPRI), a private consortium of major utility corporations that spent $10 million to investigate cold fusion. Passell disclosed disturbing information on the integrity of some of the panel members:

> When the [Department of Energy] panel came through with Huizenga as the chairman, on July 6, 1989, to visit, they were looking very lightly at the heat measurements and very strongly at the absence of neutrons and tritium. [Scientists working for EPRI] had already admitted there were none. Obviously, [they] were still alive. My feeling was that, once they saw no neutrons and tritium, they used that [fact] to denounce the field and protect their [hot fusion] budget.
>
> And fascinatingly, a couple of the people on that panel came to me ... even before the panel had finished ... looking for research funds in the field, even though publicly, they were speaking before Congress against having Congress put any money in it. Which goes to prove to you that the search for money in research is a very big thing, and it sometimes takes precedence over the search for what we would call

pure truth."[3]

In a similarly hypocritical fashion, shortly before March 2003, a prominent nuclear physicist who works at the Lawrence Livermore National Laboratory (who shall go unnamed) reviewed a paper by a top cold fusion scientist that had been submitted to a peer-reviewed journal. His public comments on the paper under review reportedly were unfavorable. Yet he then privately sought his own funding from the government sponsor of the researcher's work to pursue his *own* work in the same area identified in the paper that he had unfavorably reviewed. Six months later, this person, while speaking with a prominent cold fusion researcher, justified his actions by stating that he did not wish to be the one leading the charge by supporting cold fusion prematurely, because this would soil his reputation in the physics community.[4]

Cold fusion is a story of hundreds of men and a few women throughout the world who have demonstrated tremendous courage and willingness to take risks and make sacrifices on behalf of science and society. It is also a story of others whose desires for acceptance, certainty, status and self-preservation directed them otherwise.

CHAPTER THIRTEEN

False Debunking

"It appears that the people who would benefit most by this work being discredited have taken the initiative to cause us great difficulty. .. They might cause us difficulty, but they will not stop the science." [1]

- Dr. Stanley Pons, co-discoverer of cold fusion, former chairman of the Department of Chemistry, University of Utah

The so-called replications performed at the highly respected laboratories of Caltech, MIT and Harwell, which reportedly disproved cold fusion, created an immensely negative impact on the world's perception of this nascent field.

Once the dust had settled from the 1989 cold fusion storm, some perceived that the initial tumultuous days of cold fusion's entrance into the public arena just didn't make sense. How could cold fusion be real in one laboratory yet not in another? How could it show up in one part of the world but not in other countries? And how could some of the most prestigious laboratories in the world seemingly fail to replicate the effect while others were successful? Was any of this truly good science?

The answers appeared in no less than eight separate studies over the next four years, conducted by eight different teams of scientists.

Unlike the initial race to prove (or disprove) cold fusion, these investigators had the benefit of several quiet years of cold fusion research experience from which to benefit. In contrast, the work at Caltech, MIT, and Harwell was performed under the glare of the world's television spotlights and media attention and, for the most part, in only a few weeks.

Figure 2-10 shows the eight studies that performed "post-mortem" analyses on some of the famous laboratories' experiments, which claimed to observe no evidence for cold fusion.

Year	Caltech	MIT	Harwell
1991	Possible Excess Power (2) Major Errors(2)	Major Errors (2)	Major Errors (2)
1991		Possible Excess Power (3)	
1992			Possible Excess Power (4)
1993	Possible Excess Power (5) Major Errors (5)	Major Errors(5)	
1993	Possible Excess Power (6) Major Errors (6)		
1993	Major Errors (7)	Possible Excess Power (7)	
1994	Major Errors (8)		Major Errors (8)
1994	Major Errors (9)	Major Errors (9)	Major Errors (9)

Figure 2-10. Analysis of Early Studies that Supposedly Disproved Cold Fusion (See Endnotes [2-9])

As shown by the two values in the chart, "Possible Excess Power" and "Major Errors," the purported evidence against cold fusion is riddled with error. Furthermore, in complete contradiction to what these laboratories claimed, other researchers, with the benefit of hindsight and experience suggest that these labs actually corroborated, rather than disproved, Fleischmann and Pons' discovery!

A 1991 team of government scientists with the Naval Air Warfare Center

Weapons Division at China Lake, California, re-examined the results from Harwell, Caltech and MIT. The team found that all three "contain serious errors that will ultimately undermine the acceptance of these studies as credible electrochemical calorimetry." They also concluded that "excess power effects could easily have gone undetected in [these three] early studies." [10]

None of the analysts stated that excess power was proved in these studies; however, sufficient evidence was noted to indicate the very faint possibility that cold fusion may have occurred right under the noses of the hasty experimenters in these prestigious laboratories. Some of these analyses have been published, with no published rebuttal, in *Fusion Technology*, the *Journal of Physical Chemistry*, and the *Journal of Electroanalytical Chemistry*.

One of the first to start asking questions was Dr. Michael Melich, a senior research professor at the U.S. Naval Postgraduate School and the former branch head of the U.S. Naval Research Laboratory. Tall and wiry, Melich is dead serious and intense when he speaks about cold fusion. If pressed, he eloquently expresses his frustration with the neglect of the general scientific community toward cold fusion. "It's all just a parlor game," he said at the 10th International Conference on Cold Fusion in Cambridge, Massachusetts He attends the cold fusion conferences to track its progress but is not directly involved himself. Instead, he spends his time working with the design of phased-array antenna systems for the U.S. Navy. It is reasonable that Melich would be frustrated - he's done his homework.

Early on, Melich was suspicious of the level of integrity with which the scientific community had evaluated the claims of cold fusion. In 1992, he began a thorough investigation of the laboratories whose refutations provided the so-called proof against the validity of the Fleischmann-Pons effect.[11]

Melich gathered a team of five researchers to review the quality of these experiments and perform independent analyses of their original data. In his travels, he found that the Harwell team, led by electrochemist David Williams, had performed the best work among the various laboratories. Williams was very cooperative and willing to provide the original data for Melich's analysis. He also authorized Melich to hire Harwell's lead experimentalist to work on the review and perform all-new analyses.[12]

The team found two things of significance. As Melich says diplomatically, in light of the "extreme public scrutiny" during the 1989 media firestorm, the Harwell scientists "had little opportunity to ... mature their instruments or procedures and fully understand the requirements for the experiments." [13]

As well, careful analysis revealed that, in one of the cold fusion cells, there were "more than ten time intervals where an unexplained power source or energy storage mechanism may [have been] operating." In fact, *Melich noted possible excess energy in magnitudes similar to that reported by Fleischmann and Pons.* In an attempt to inform the scientific world, which was intent on rejecting the cold fusion effect, he warned, "Scientists have no business using the Harwell data to reject the Fleischmann-Pons effect!" [14]

In private conversations, Melich speaks and writes carefully to avoid openly criticizing other scientists, being sensitive to avoid another public mêlée. But after traveling with a team of five scientists to southern California, he met with such disappointment that he had acute criticism for the Caltech laboratory.

For unknown reasons, his access to the raw data was obstructed.[15] From the sparse data he was able to obtain, Melich observed that the Caltech team, under the direction of Lewis and physicist Charlie Barnes,[16] clearly "did not spend the time to understand the subtleties of the Fleischmann-Pons experiment."

While some aspects of the Caltech work were excellent, Melich sharply criticized its calorimetry, its experimental design and its analysis of the results. [17]

In discussions with Lewis, Melich perceived that he had poor oversight of the calorimetry work and was unable to respond to the documented problems with the Caltech work.[18] Lewis himself admitted to having trouble with calorimetry: "Heat was confusing to nearly everyone, including all my electrochemical friends." [19]

Fleischmann remembers Lewis constantly calling Pons for help:

> I had gone back to the U.K., I was disgusted with the whole thing, and Stan phoned me up and said, "This man [Lewis] keeps on phoning me up, and he doesn't take any notice of what I say." But since he is a fellow electrochemist, you know, we made the best effort to answer his questions.

When Fleischmann originally saw the published Caltech work, he was skeptical:

> The first thing I do when I am a referee of a paper is that I try to work out how much time they actually had to do the work. Caltech couldn't possibly have done this properly in the given time frame, as they so adamantly claimed. The Harwell work was absolutely honest, but the work from Caltech was completely dishonest. They should never have done that work.[20]

Dr. Robert Bass, a physicist formerly with the hot fusion program at Princeton Plasma Physics Laboratory, recalled learning about another scientist who audited the Caltech cold fusion work:

> Dr. Noninsky, an internationally distinguished calorimetrist, asked to see Caltech's raw data and reanalyzed it. He proved that, even though Caltech researchers had incompetently not bothered to attain any of the Fleischmann-Pons "minimum thresholds" for good experiments, they had still attained 10 percent or so excess heat at Caltech, but they just didn't want to admit it. Dr. Noninski's papers exposing the bungle at Caltech have been refused to be published by *Science* and *Nature*, though there are no identifiable mistakes in his work.[21]

David Lindley, associate editor of *Nature,* made the astonishingly unethical decision to send the paper that had been submitted by *Noninsky* to *Lewis* for his review! Unsurprisingly, Lewis recommended against the publication of a critique against his own work. Lindley, convinced that cold fusion was a worthless cause, sent this reply to Noninsky:

> I am sorry that we must persist in our negative opinion of your work, but it seems clear by now that you are not pursuing a useful path. I can see no likelihood that *Nature* would wish to publish your work.

And so with careless and arrogant regard for the scientific method, one of the most prestigious science journals in the world added yet another course of bricks to wall off this truly novel discovery, in defense of the status quo.[22]

Independent of Noninski's analysis, Dr. Melvin Miles, then the lead electrochemist for the U.S. Navy's China Lake cold fusion team, conducted his own post-mortem on the Caltech cold fusion bungle. Miles concluded in a letter written to John Maddox, editor of *Nature*, that, "contrary to the claims of [Lewis and Miskelly at Caltech], a study of this nature is completely incapable of proving that no anomalous power was produced." [23]

In his paper published in the *Journal of Physical Chemistry,* Miles concluded the following with regard to the Caltech results:

> An excess power effect develops that becomes as large as 0.076 W after 161 hours of Pd/D_2O + LiOD electrolysis. The excess power density of 1.0 W/cm3 Pd for this analysis of the N. Lewis study is in excellent agreement with our experiments (1.3 W/cm3 Pd at 200 mA/cm2) as well as with the results reported by M. Fleischmann et al. in 1990.[24]

McKubre at SRI International expressed his view on what happened at Caltech:

> The way that Nate Lewis conducted his calorimetry was just wrong. It was amateurish and silly, actually. What he did was change his calibration every day to make sure that the excess heat was zero; he changed his calibration with the assertion that the answer is zero, so by definition he observed zero every day, even though he had to change his calibration constant to do it.

I think it was a semi legitimate thing for an ignorant and impatient man. Every day they came in, and the calorimetry was either producing positive excess heat or negative excess heat, both of which were unbelievable to Lewis, so that what they did was change the calibration constant so that it went away.[25]

The *Journal of Electroanalytical Chemistry, Fusion Technology,* and the *Journal of Physical Chemistry* each published Miles' analysis of the botched Caltech cold fusion experiment.[26]

Miles believes the opportunity for rebuttal was made available to Lewis, as is standard journalistic practice, but that Lewis "apparently didn't want to debate the point." Miles said, "He just wanted to let it all slide away and disappear." [27]

Within a five-year period after the Caltech cold fusion experiments, at least five teams of scientists had performed retrospective analyses of the Caltech cold fusion work, and all of them found numerous errors. Both Noninski and the China Lake team concluded that Caltech's results may have *replicated* rather than disproved the claims of Fleischmann and Pons.

CHAPTER FOURTEEN

MIT's Fumbled (or Worse) Experiments

"No cover-up like this has happened before. It is a profound scandal in American science."

- Charles Beaudette, author, *Excess Heat & Why Cold Fusion Research Prevailed*

Historically, MIT's cold fusion work has been considered one of the most significant of the early studies that discredited cold fusion. Its influence stems from the fact that the U.S. Patent and Trademark Office cites MIT's "proof" of the nonexistence of cold fusion as the reason for categorically rejecting all cold fusion-related patent applications. This policy has had a deadening impact on American research in the field. The lack of intellectual property protection makes investment in cold fusion research unwise and thereby discourages private investment in cold fusion research. Japan, by contrast, has issued cold fusion patents.

Three groups of researchers performed post-hoc analyses of the MIT experiments; they found flaws not unlike those of Harwell and Caltech. Two of the groups identified possible evidence of excess heat, the key indicator of cold fusion, in the MIT results.

One of these teams was led by Eugene Mallove who, during the spring of 1991, had been finishing the first book on cold fusion, *Fire From Ice: Searching for the Truth Behind the Cold Fusion Furor*. At the time, he was the chief science writer with the MIT News office. The public attacks on

Fleischmann and Pons and other scientists pursuing cold fusion research were still quite aggressive.

By then, many had concluded that Fleischmann and Pons were charlatans, and some believed it was their God-given duty to expose them. The Boston Herald quoted Dr. Ronald Parker, a key figure at MIT:

> Everything I've been able to track down has been bogus, and I think we owe it to the community of scientists to begin to smoke these guys out.[1]

The MIT scientists "were claiming all along that they had done a very solid experiment in calorimetry," Mallove said. They said that their experiments were identical (or better) than that of Fleischmann and Pons but that theirs showed no excess heat.[2]

What initially tipped Mallove off to a problem were two differing draft reports given to him casually by one of the staff at the Plasma Fusion Center, which had run the original MIT cold fusion experiment. Mallove was astounded:

> I could see immediately that there was a serious discrepancy between the unpublished, pre-processed raw data [in these documents] and the final published data.[3]

Mallove gave the graphs to Dr. Mitchell Swartz to conduct his own independent study and quantitative analysis of the data. Swartz is also a Harvard and MIT graduate. He concluded that a "bias was introduced into the [graphs which] obscured the generation of heat." [4]

Mallove could see no explanation for this bias. From his viewpoint, the published MIT report was "*arbitrarily shifted downward to make the apparent excess heat vanish.*" [6]

He expressed his dismay over the situation:

> In the case of MIT, it was a disaster. These people, before even analyzing their calorimetry data, held a party for the death of cold fusion. And then they unfortunately fudged the data and manipulated

the data to make a positive result look negative. At the very least, the people at MIT had an obligation to go back and check their experiment again. Their results don't prove cold fusion, but they certainly had a positive result.

Mallove blamed a conflict of interest for clouding the judgment of the MIT Plasma Fusion Center staff. They receive tens of millions of dollars per year in funding for hot fusion research. Mallove had no reservations about condemning the actions of those who manipulated the data:

> Some would characterize the data manipulation in the sixteen- author MIT paper of 1989 as mere "data fudging." We do not mince words. The use of improperly handled scientific data to draw in the public mind and in the mind of the scientific community a completely false conclusion about an emerging discovery of overarching importance to humankind is high-level scientific misconduct, plain and simple.[7]

Figures 2-11.1 through 2-11.6 show three sets of graphs displaying the results of the MIT cold fusion experiments. The graphs compare an experimental cold fusion cell using heavy water to a control cell using light water. The first two graphs show the original, unpublished data as it appeared in documents dated July 10, 1989. The second two graphs show interpreted data from documents dated July 13, 1989.[8] The third set of graphs, created by Dr. Swartz,[9] provides overlays of the first two sets. Shown in this way, the unbalanced handling of the interpreted reports becomes more evident.

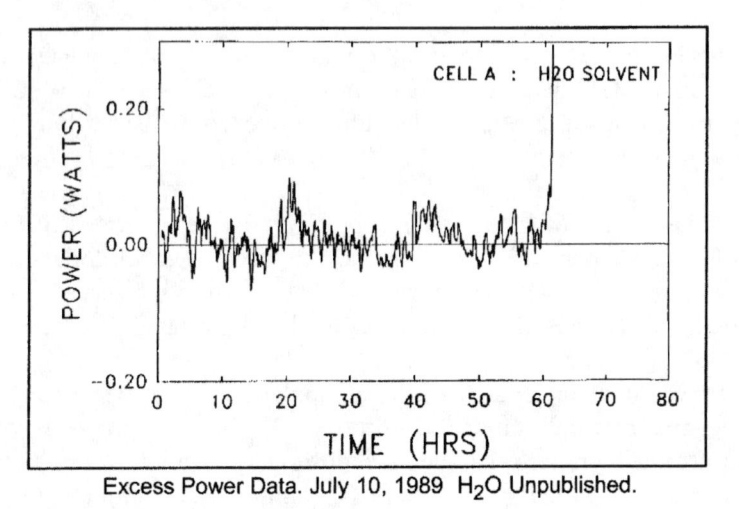

Excess Power Data. July 10, 1989 H_2O Unpublished.

Figure 2-11.1. Graph showing MIT heat measurements for the control cell using light water. The signal represents the original, unpublished data from July 10, 1989, documents. The signal averages along the baseline.

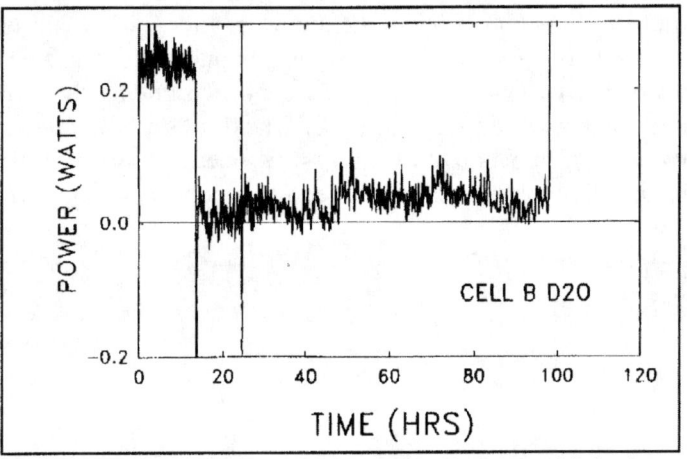

Excess Power Data. July 10, 1989 D_2O Unpublished.

Figure 2-11.2. Graph showing MIT heat measurements for the experimental cold fusion cell using heavy water. The signal represents the original, unpublished data from July 10, 1989, documents. The signal is significantly above the baseline.

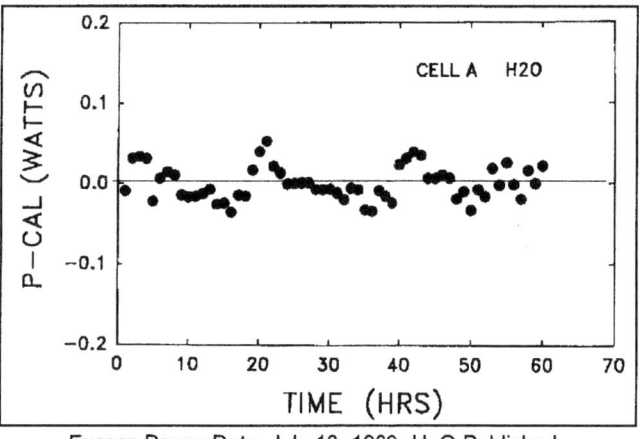

Excess Power Data. July 13, 1989 H_2O Published

Figure 2-11.3. Graph showing MIT heat measurements for the control cell using light water. The points represent the interpreted, published data from July 13, 1989, documents. The points average along the baseline.

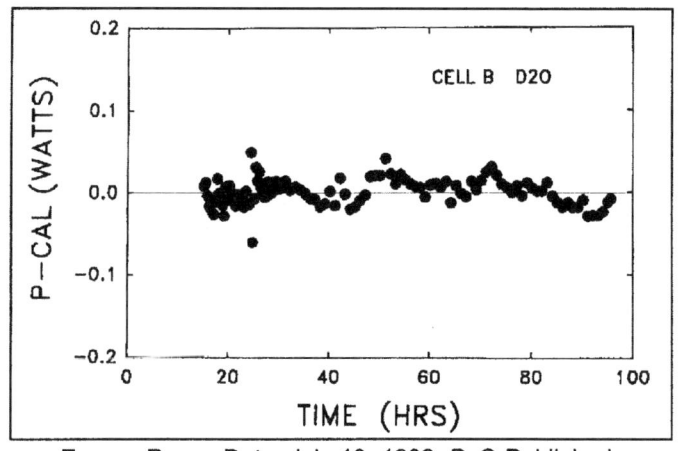

Excess Power Data. July 13, 1989 D_2O Published.

Figure 2-11.4. Graph showing MIT heat measurements for the experimental cold fusion cell using heavy water. The points represent the interpreted, published data from July 13, 1989, documents. The points average along the baseline.

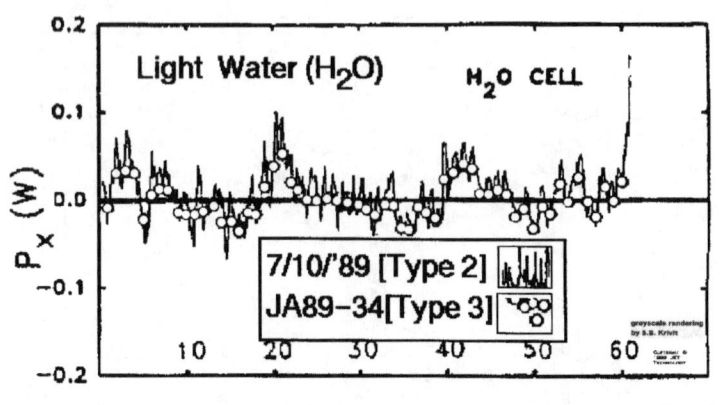

Figure 2-11.5. Overlay graph showing heat measurements for the control cell, using light water. The solid continuous line represents the original, unpublished data from July 10. The open circles represent the published, interpreted data from July 13. This figure shows basic agreement between the two. (Image Courtesy of Mitchell Swartz, Jet Technologies)

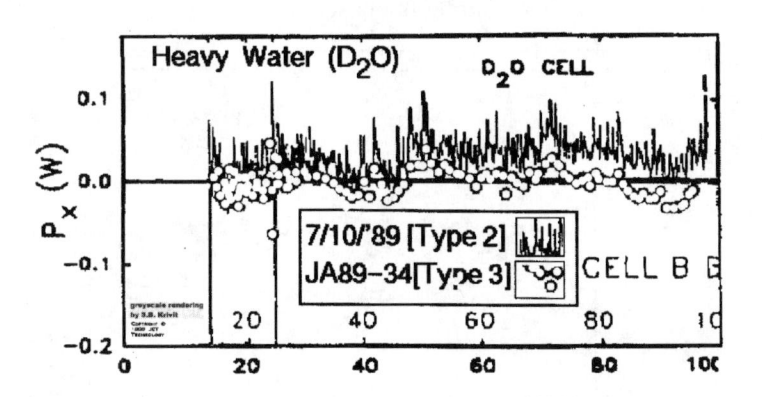

Figure 2-11.6. Overlay graph showing heat measurements for the experimental cold fusion cell using heavy water. The solid continuous line represents the original, unpublished data from July 10. The open circles represent the published, interpreted data from July 13. This graph has been manipulated and reflects a downward adjustment in the interpretation of the data. (Image Courtesy of Mitchell Swartz, Jet Technologies)

Both Swartz and Mallove pursued the matter through letters to the president of MIT. Mallove received no response. Swartz did, perhaps because of his previous MIT inventions, the large amount of data and information that accompanied his letter, or his contribution in helping to set up the MIT Innovation Center. Swartz said that, in response, "the president of MIT directed the plasma fusion center to give me the information I requested." Swartz said, "I received data from a total of three places, including two that Gene didn't have access to, as well as confidential information shared with me by Professor Ronald Parker." [10]

"After [MIT] President Vest received my report," Swartz says, "he asked Philip Morrison to review it." Morrison is an MIT Professor Emeritus of physics who played a key role in the Manhattan project. Swartz continued, "After reviewing and corroborating my report, Morrison subsequently wrote his own report to President Vest."

Morrison's [Aug. 18, 1991] letter to Vest stated that he found "mean power excess: heavy water cell - +15 milliwatts, light water cell - +4 milliwatts" with regard to the July 10, 1989, graphs. He stated that the "13 July draft ... ends up with a value I did not measure, but one visibly close to zero for both cells." He concluded, "making these few numbers publicly available ... would for me fairly and helpfully clear the record."

Swartz noted that, to this day, MIT has never followed Morrison's advice. What the university did, in May 1992, was to publish a "Technical Appendix" written by only one of the original 14 authors of the MIT cold fusion paper, Stanley Luckhardt. The Technical Appendix explained that, in retrospect, the original MIT cold fusion team had interpreted the appearance of heat within their study as merely an artifact of instrumentation error. He stated that they had made "corrections" at the time to "clarify" the data.

Swartz elucidated these unusual inconsistencies in scientific protocol:

> Much current skepticism of the cold fusion phenomenon was created by the [MIT Plasma Fusion Center] paper's reporting "failure-to-reproduce" as opposed to its later claimed "too-insensitive-to-confirm" experiments. Because it may be the single most widely quoted work used by critics of cold fusion to dismiss the phenomena,

the paper should have clarified all "data" points and the methodology used. In addition, apparent curve proliferation, volatile points, symmetric curve shifts, in combination with an impaired methodology have needlessly degraded the sensitivity and believability of the [MIT] calorimetry experiment. [11]

They [tried] to backpedal, [but] ... their own data does show confirmation of cold fusion. They should have published their positive results or have been more honest about what they did to the heavy water curve. [12]

Swartz stated, "I wrote a second report and submitted it to the president. This, then, was a total of three reports which all went to President Vest. But they never took any action; they should have either retracted just the one curve [graph] or the entire paper." [13]

Storms explained in a November 2003 telephone conversation that, understandably, MIT assumed that its calorimetric instruments and methods matched those of Fleischmann and Pons. Only years later did the scientific community learn that the Utah electrochemists had developed a very sophisticated analytical method which was, in fact, far superior. In addition, they had engineered a calorimeter capable of detecting excess heat in tiny quantities, with an error range of plus or minus 1 milliwatt. In contrast, the calorimeter used by MIT was able to discriminate excess heat at levels no better than plus or minus 40 milliwatts. MIT's calorimeter was less precise than Fleischmann and Pons' *by an order of magnitude*.

Nevertheless, MIT researchers failed to follow accepted data reporting practices. They should have provided the original results along with their interpretation, "artifact of instrumentation error." Had they done so, accusations of data manipulation would have been avoided. Instead, they replotted the data and created the false impression that the raw data demonstrated zero excess heat. "Since the entire purpose of the experiment was to determine whether or not there was an excess-heat effect," Storms said in a telephone conversation, "the consequences of shifting the data are immense." [14]

As with Caltech's and Harwell's experiments, the MIT study should have indicated summarily that the evidence for the excess heat effect was inconclusive. Instead, MIT firmly stated a negative impression focusing on the absence of nuclear products.

The quality of MIT's neutron detection work has not been in question and in fact has been described as outstanding. The problem derives from the fact that neutrons and tritium, the dominant nuclear products predicted by traditional fusion theory, are not the only possible nuclear fusion products. In fact, helium-4, which is extremely rare in hot fusion, turns out to be the most common nuclear product in cold fusion. To its credit, the MIT team did attempt to detect helium-4, both in the effluent gases and in the palladium rod. But so far as the detection limits of their equipment would allow, they were unable to observe helium levels above background. Unfortunately, they used glass cells, which are not ideal for the capture of helium because of its permeability to the gas.

Mallove resigned from his job at the MIT news office as a result of MIT's handling of cold fusion. Jed Rothwell wrote, "This was an extraordinary thing to do! Call it brave, or call it quixotic, very few middle-class people with a comfortable, prestigious job at a world-famous institution would resign over a matter of principle, in an obscure scientific debate. But Gene did not hesitate."

It was not simply the matter of data fudging that offended Mallove's principles and compelled him to resign. Swartz, a close colleague of Mallove's explained:

> Gene quit because there were two underlying events that enraged him. First, the matter of the [April 28, 1989] Nick Tate interview with Ronald Parker [see below]. The other thing that upset Gene was that, even after we had given them my report - I gave two reports to the president, one of which was corroborated by Philip Morrison in his own report - *there was no follow-through.*[15]

On April 28, 1989, two of the lead scientists on the MIT Plasma Fusion Center team gave an interview to journalist Nick Tate of the *Boston Herald*. The allegations made by Parker and Ballinger were clear. They had taken a publicly hostile position on the known errors made by Fleischmann and Pons concerning the Utah neutron measurements, which were indeed incorrect and poorly done.

But they went far beyond dispassionate objectivity and made incendiary and defamatory remarks to Tate, who reported exactly what they told him. Nearly every facet of this complex drama is documented by Mallove in his "MIT and Cold Fusion: A Special Report," which is available on the Web at www.infinite-energy.com. Comments made by Parker and Ballinger throughout the interview include the following:

> - This is scientific schlock.
> - They've misinterpreted their results.
> - They falsely interpreted their results.
> - It's fraud.

An unpublished comment by Parker that Mallove heard a year later when listening to the tape recording of the interview caused Mallove to suspect that Parker and Ballinger intentionally used the news media to further their own position in the cold fusion debate. This is what Parker told the reporter:

> We think it's a scam. ... We have been studying the evidence together very slowly, and we want to have a paper out on this before we actually blast them. Monday, we're putting a paper out on it. ... It depends on what magnitude you want to break it.

"Historically," Mallove wrote, "it is evident that this *Herald* story helped unleash the tidal wave of negativity against Fleischmann and Pons and others who continue to work in the field."

However, long before Mallove would gain access to the tape recording, he explained events which occurred two days after the interview, on the eve of the publication of the story:

> A frantic Ronald Parker, perhaps fearing that he would be sued by Pons and Fleischmann for the harsh words that were quoted a bit too explicitly for his taste, called me late on the night of April 30, 1989.

> I had been up into the wee hours of the night of April 30-May 1, 1989, sending a press release dictated to me over the telephone at my home in Bow, New Hampshire, by Parker. [Mallove writes that

112

Parker was tipped off to the exact nature of the story by a call from CBS television.]

I telephoned [the press release] to UPI, Reuters, and the Associated Press, and it denied what Parker had said in the interview with the Boston Herald's Nick Tate. When I arrived at the MIT News Office early that morning after a sleepless night, we hastily put together a printed form of the press release to handle the approaching storm. This is the text of the press release that was issued from the MIT News Office on May 1, 1989:

MIT News Office PRESS RELEASE May 1, 1989
URGENT MEDIA ADVISORY
For Immediate Release May 1, 1989
MIT Contact: Eugene F. Mallove,
Sc.D. Chief Science Writer

CAMBRIDGE, Mass., May 1—Professor Ronald R. Parker, Director of the MIT Plasma Fusion Center responded today to an article published this morning in the Boston Herald, an article that he says has seriously misquoted him and given a largely incorrect view of his discussions with the Boston Herald's reporter, Nick Tate.

Professor Parker issued this statement:

"The article erroneously characterizes remarks that I made regarding the cold fusion experiments done at the University of Utah. Specifically, I did not: (1) Deride the University of Utah experiments as "scientific schlock" or (2) Accuse Drs. Fleischmann and Pons of 'misrepresentation and maybe fraud.'"

Today, Professor Parker's colleagues will present a paper (co-authored with him) at the meeting of the American Physical Society in Baltimore, Maryland, in which they suggest that data that Drs. Pons and Fleischmann claim support the observation of neutron emission in their experiments were misinterpreted by Pons and Fleischmann."

Of course, I had at that time no reason to doubt what he was telling me, that the story was a distortion [allegedly by Tate at the Herald]. I would learn the stark truth about this deception only over a year later when Tate allowed me to listen to the actual tape.

When Mallove heard the tape, he realized not only that Parker had lied to him about Tate allegedly misquoting Parker but also that Parker had used Mallove to convey his own misdeeds:

On the day of my resignation from my MIT News Office position, June 7, 1991, I publicly disavowed this Press Release [which I was directed to write. It was] an unintended falsification of the truth in which I was used as a dupe in part of an orchestrated campaign against cold fusion.

Matters came to a head on [June 7, 1991], when, unknown to me until the very few days before it occurred, a lecture by a strong critic of cold fusion, Dr. Frank Close of the U.K., was scheduled for a Friday seminar at the Plasma Fusion Center. The posters for the talk proclaimed it to be "An Exposé on Cold Fusion," and indeed, it was just that: a slanderous attack on Fleischmann and Pons! It turned out to be a climactic event in my career and in the history of cold fusion.

The final straw, Swartz says, may have come for Mallove at the end of the lecture, during the question and answer section. Mallove made two efforts to discuss the shifted curves but was rebuffed by Parker:

You can redraw those curves anyway that you want. I don't think that data is worth anything.

Mallove responded with his last and final effort to encourage MIT to take a sincere look at cold fusion:

MIT ought to take a look at it again. That's the only thing that will ultimately clear this up. I don't agree that passion and PR and so forth should solve this; I think experiments should, but they are not being done here.

Frank Close then jumped in and responded with the brush-off, "It's one o'clock and we've got to go to a luncheon." Before Mallove could get in another word, the MIT Plasma Fusion Center's Richard Petrasso announced the end of the talk and thanked the audience for coming.

"Gene wanted to respond with a rebuttal because there were things Close was saying that were absolutely untrue," Swartz remembered. 'But they cut him off and refused to let him speak further." This appeared to be the final event that triggered his resignation. "Gene just stood up and publicly announced his resignation from MIT at that point," research engineer Mike Staker recalled.

115

In a sad ending to this chapter of cold fusion history and to Mallove's historic struggle with scientific orthodoxy, Mallove was tragically and senselessly murdered in May 2004 in what police believe was a robbery gone awry. He will be remembered as a courageous champion of truth and a fighter for the purity of science. He also will be known for his clear and persistent voice of reason, his tremendous personal and professional sacrifices and his accomplishments on behalf of the worldwide cold fusion research effort.

CHAPTER FIFTEEN

Corroborating Evidence

The bungling of the Caltech, MIT and Harwell experiments went unnoticed by most outside of the cold fusion community. Likewise, several notable confirmations of the claims, achieved over the first six years, were unreported.

Over the course of eight investigations, the hidden evidence slowly revealed itself. Of those who conducted these studies, some were proponents who were thrilled to witness this evidence unfold; others were cynics who probably were dismayed by it.

Figure 2-12 illustrates the various cold fusion experiments that corroborated the claims. The experiments are listed along the top by researcher or laboratory. Each row represents individual scientific reports, some of which are formal papers and others of which are unpublished and previously undisclosed private reports. Two types of reports are listed: papers by the experimenters describing their own *experimental* work, and reports by third parties, who performed *analysis* of others' work.

The findings given in this chart display evidence that supports the Fleischmann-Pons claims. First, confirmations of *excess power* are shown. Second, the two nuclear byproducts - the dominant product, helium-4, and the lesser product, tritium - are shown. A milestone finding, wherein excess heat and helium were correlated, is also shown. The significance of this correlation will be covered in greater detail in Part Three of this book. The last finding is of two reports that conclude that the observed effect cannot possibly be the result of a chemical reaction.

Cold Fusion Corroborations

Year	Fleischmann & Pons	Oriani	U.S. Navy	Amoco	Shell	SRI Int'l
1990 Exper.		**Excess Power** (1)				
1991 Analysis	**Excess Power** Not Chem. (2)					
1991 Analysis						**Excess Power** No Major Errors (3)
1993 Exper.			**Excess Power** Correlated Heat and Helium (4)			
1993 Analysis						**Excess Power** No Major Errors, Not Chem. (5)
1994 Analysis	**Excess Power** (6)			**Excess Power** Tritium (6)		
1995 Exper.					**Excess Power** Helium (7)	
1995 Exper.				**Excess Power** Tritium Not Chem. (8)		

Figure 2-12. Cold Fusion Corroborations (See Endnotes [1-8])

The U.S. Navy's Melich reviewed several of these studies during his investigation of the cold fusion claims. He learned that, in 1990, Wilford Hansen was commissioned by the Utah Fusion Energy Council to head a committee to analyze the original Fleischmann and Pons data.

Hansen earned his Ph.D. in physical chemistry from Iowa State University in 1956 and pursued studies in physics. His first job was working for North American Aviation (which later became part of Rockwell International) in its science center. His first academic assignment was as a professor of chemistry at Brigham Young University. Later, he had a joint appointment in physics and chemistry at Utah State University.

In Hansen's review, he used computerized data analysis to avoid potential errors resulting from human analysis of calorimetry data. On completion of his analysis, Hansen reported that the quantity of excess energy found in the Fleischmann-Pons cells was "over a thousand times the energy required to vaporize the electrode." The significance of Hansen's analysis was clear:

> It is easy to see that we are not dealing with known chemistry or metallurgy. At issue is a profound energy source.[9]

In concluding his own investigation, Melich cautioned those who would listen:

> An observation that simply fails to answer "yes" (call it "negative") does not answer "no." It simply gives no answer at all. Yet simple negative results have been taken as convincing evidence that the [Fleischmann-Pons effect] does not exist. And current patent and funding policies are driven by a few negative results. ... The challenge to science is to solve the case, with hard work and rational dialogue. We should not allow such a smoke screen to be thrown up that the answers can't be recognized even when they are found. We also must be careful that our motives are purely scientific."[10]

Melich also evaluated the unpublished work of scientists at Amoco Oil Corporation. He noted that, in contrast to the Harwell and Caltech experiments, the 1989 Amoco experiments, which had been performed outside of the glare of publicity, were conducted with patience, care and

119

precision. The Amoco team was able to complete three iterations of experimentation, sequentially improving and maturing its experimental instruments and designs. The result was "large steady levels of heat, as well as bursts of heat, at magnitudes 100 to 1,000 times greater than instrumental error" and tritium levels which increased by a factor of three after electrolysis.[11]

The findings of small amounts of tritium at levels significantly higher than the background levels is a major set of evidence supporting claims of nuclear reactions in cold fusion experiments. The Amoco scientists concluded their private report using vague references to avoid the stigma of cold fusion:

> These data support the claims of several experimenters [that is, Fleischmann and Pons] that anomalous heat and tritium are produced during electrolytic experiments using a hydrogen-absorbing [that is, palladium] cathode [in other words, cold fusion].[12]

Since 1989, Shell Oil has maintained an active interest in cold fusion research. Until Jacques Dufour retired from Shell in 1993, he led the research group in its cold fusion experiments.

Dufour is a physicist and chemist with credentials from one of the "Grande Ecole's" in France, Ecole Nationale Supérieure des Mines de Paris. He held the title of director of scientific relations for the Shell research group in France. While there, he was awarded three patents: one in the field of hydrocarbon processing, and two in the field of cold fusion.

Since 1993, Dufour has continued his cold fusion work at Conservatoire National des Arts et Métiers in the Laboratoire des Sciences Nucléaires, which has, on occasion, received continued research funding from Shell. Since that time, Dufour has published a dozen papers and has been awarded a fourth patent in cold fusion.

In a 1995 presentation to the 5th International Conference on Cold Fusion, describing his measurements with a 99 percent level of confidence, Dufour concluded, "Excess energy production was confirmed in the simple [Fleischmann and Pons] system ... up to several watts." [13]

In Dufour's view, the lack of a 100 percent reproducible experiment is the greatest challenge for the field. He expressed this objective for himself: "From the results I have now, I don't exclude the possibility of getting such an experiment within six to twelve months."[14]

In what may seem a surprising comment to those anticipating a conspiracy, Dufour said he doesn't "feel any will from Shell to block the development of this new source of energy." In his view, Shell sees its company role as "energy providers" rather than merely "petroleum providers." Dufour noted, "As a former Shell man, I know that this development will take tens of years to have a significant impact."[15]

In mid-1990, the Amoco scientists discontinued their experimentation because of early reproducibility problems and a lack of accounting between the excess heat and the nuclear products. In late 2003, however, one of the researchers who worked with the Amoco team, Melvin Eisner, developed renewed interest in performing cold fusion research after learning of recent developments in the field. In a February 2004 e-mail, the physics professor emeritus from the University of Houston stated that, in light of better understanding regarding the different nuclear products observed in cold vs. hot fusion, he and his former Amoco colleague, Theodore Lautzenhiser, have decided to resume experimentation.[16]

CHAPTER SIXTEEN

Cold Fusion: A Forbidden Topic

"The general public must learn that science doesn't work the way they think it does - universities are not really the bastions of free academic speech that they purport to be."

- Dennis Letts, Alternate Energy Researcher, Austin, Texas[1]

With such strong support in many scientific corners, it seems hard to believe that the results of cold fusion experiments have remained hidden, but that is exactly the case. In spite of the fact that 3,000 scientific papers have been written on cold fusion, progress has been underreported because of a rift between cold fusion researchers and the scientific establishment, whose most prominent journals still refuse to publish papers relating to cold fusion. Instead, publication of cold fusion papers has taken an "open source" approach and can be freely downloaded from the Web. See www.lenr-canr.org, for example.

As a side note, for those unfamiliar with the significance of scientific publishing, having one's paper published in a peer-reviewed journal means everything to a scientist. Having the most important revolutionary and demonstrable experiment does a scientist little good if he or she fails to get it published. If the paper does not get published, it likely will never be seen by the scientific community and, consequently, may just as well not exist.

Other scientists rarely take seriously papers published in non-peer- reviewed journals. As well, managers of research funds and grants, who provide the lifeblood of scientific research, also bypass these papers.

Some cold fusion papers do continue to be published, albeit in obscure, highly specialized journals. *The Japanese Journal of Applied Physics* is one of the more permissive in accepting cold fusion papers, for example. In the early days of cold fusion research, a few journals were willing to publish cold fusion papers, but those numbers have dwindled to near zero. It is an interesting paradox that, while cold fusion research has improved, more doorways to publishing have closed.

Richard Oriani is a professor emeritus from the University of Minnesota and a Ph.D. graduate in physical chemistry from Princeton University. He was among many to perform early replications of the Fleischmann and Pons excess heat effect, the most important aspect of the cold fusion discovery:

> I knew that it was a good corroboration of the original calorimetric work of Fleischmann and Pons. I was very happy about that. I began as a real skeptic in this thing because, for two months, I got nothing but negative results. Now, it is well known that intermittent results are typical of cold fusion work, though we don't know all the parameters yet. But then, suddenly, I got two wonderful results. They were real and inescapable evidence, so I became convinced.

Yet Oriani went through quite an ordeal trying to publish his paper. He and the co-authors of the work initially submitted their paper in mid-September, 1989, to the prestigious journal *Nature*. After a few back-and-forth exchanges of correspondence, *Nature* gave its final rejection. "We were irritated, of course," Oriani says of the rejection. But, he added, "we understood the problem, that this is unorthodox, this is hard to believe."

One peer reviewer rejected the paper because it failed to demonstrate nuclear evidence, and "without this, the manuscript does not contain anything except a report of an unidentified heat-producing process." The reviewer saw the evidence of cold fusion but failed to recognize its potential significance. The comment was akin to saying, "The Wright brothers' invention failed to demonstrate anything except an unidentified method of suspending a human body in the air!" The reviewers' second reason for rejection was that no explanation for the heat was given. Oriani sees the response as a failure to adhere to the principles of the scientific method:

The irritation also came about because the editors, not only of *Nature* but also of other magazines, insisted on having a theory that goes along with the results. And that is not really the natural way that science progresses. One publishes an experimental result, either with or without an idea of what is underlying those results, hoping that other people will get interested and contribute their ideas experimentally and theoretically. The idea is to disseminate the phenomena so that other people can collaborate to generate a good theory. But that's not what happened in this case. It was very irritating, very maddening. [2]

Considering that this paper documented the most profound aspect of the Fleischmann-Pons discovery, the excess heat effect, *Nature's* rejection letter finished with a most puzzling statement: "*Nature* is certainly happy to publish papers which shed light on cold fusion ... however, your paper seems likely to add to the confusion rather than to enlighten." [3]

Eventually, Oriani succeeded in getting his paper, "Calorimetric Measurements of Excess Power Output During the Cathodic Charging of Deuterium Into Palladium," published, but in the journal *Fusion Technology*. A decade later, things got even tougher.[4]

Miles performed extensive cold fusion research while with the U.S. Naval Air Warfare Center Weapons Division at China Lake, California. He lists 194 published papers to his credit and is the author of 17 U.S. patents.

Miles had an early exposure to chemistry. His father was a chemistry teacher for many years at Dixie College, in Miles' hometown of St. George, Utah. Miles attended the college for his undergraduate studies and was honored as the valedictorian of his class. He earned his Ph.D. in physical chemistry, with a minor in physics, at the University of Utah. He noted that he had an early advantage in his initial cold fusion research:

> When I heard about the cold fusion announcement in March of 1989, I started working on it that weekend. I was already using the palladium/hydrogen system as a reference electrode on my research for the Navy.[5]

Rothwell wrote of Miles in his paper "Introduction to the Cold Fusion Experiments of Melvin Miles":

> Miles is quiet, dignified and, as Martin Fleischmann says, thoroughly honest. He was a university professor before coming to the Navy. He is not a disputatious person. He does not exaggerate or argue for the sake of arguing. He does not enjoy politics or controversy. ... Miles is a professional, and quite willing to share information, ... his lectures at the major cold fusion conferences have been models of clarity and rigor.

Figure 2-13. Dr. Melvin Miles
(Photo by Steven Krivit)

One of Miles' significant accomplishments was a key contribution to the hefty 125-page 2002 cold fusion report "Thermal and Nuclear Aspects of the Pd/D$_2$O System, A Decade of Research at Navy Laboratories," published by the U.S. Navy's Space and Naval Warfare Systems Command (SPAWAR) center in San Diego, California. Miles was a guest researcher at the Center for New Hydrogen Energy, Institute of Applied Energy, Sapporo, Japan when the Japanese government initiated a major cold fusion research effort.

The report is based on experiments Miles performed at the New Hydrogen Energy laboratory, using a special palladium-boron alloy developed by the U.S. Navy, he says. Miles explained:

> When the Navy decided to get into this officially, there were three laboratories involved: China Lake, where I worked, the SPAWAR Laboratory in San Diego, and the Naval Research Laboratory in Washington, D.C. One of the objectives of the Naval Research Laboratory was to make our own materials so we weren't dependent on outside sources. We knew that the key to making it work was a materials problem. None of the materials from Naval Research Laboratory worked for about the first two years. But as soon as Dr. Ashraf M. Imam [a metallurgist] at the Naval Research Laboratory developed the palladium-boron, I started seeing excess heat in nearly every experiment after that. I think we did about ten in total, and all but one showed excess heat. It came around the end of 1994, toward the end of the China Lake program, but because we hadn't had much success prior to that, the program had already started shutting down. I don't think they realized the significance of the materials development. But I knew it, and I knew that it was a very good material, so I took it with me to Japan and ran it there, and it produced a lot of excess heat and was the basis of the Naval Research Laboratory report.

> Stan Szpak [an electrochemist] and Pamela Mosier-Boss [a chemist], also with SPAWAR, published a report on other experiments we did in Japan which was called co-deposition, a method pioneered by Stan and Pam. In co-deposition, you don't start with any palladium metal. Instead, you start with a copper substrate as the cathode, and you add palladium salts (palladium chloride) into the solution of heavy water along with some lithium chloride, another salt that helps the palladium dissolve.

> When you run the cell, you start seeing a black, palladium material covering the copper surface as you watch it happen. It think it's almost a nanomaterial; it has a very small grain structure. All three of my co-deposition experiments in Japan produced significant excess heat.[6]

Miles presented the key aspects of the SPAWAR report in a shorter paper at the Electrochemical Society International Meeting in San Francisco in September 2001. He noted that this paper "contained important new results showing that the Naval Research Laboratory palladium-boron material readily produces the excess heat effect - the main signature of cold fusion."

What happened next is somewhat ironic. Miles, an electrochemist, submitted his paper regarding a novel electrochemical discovery for publication, and he was told by editor Paul A. Kohl that "the *Journal of The Electrochemical Society* is not a good match for your paper. ... Therefore we are returning your manuscript to you *without having reviewed it*." [italics added] [7]

Miles, not one to lash out with anger, anguished over his squelched work and contribution to society. He calmly and diplomatically wrote:

> Critics tell us that we need to publish our results in refereed scientific journals. Then when we attempt to do so, the editors of these journals tell us to take our submitted manuscripts elsewhere. Presently, there are very few "elsewheres" remaining.

> Martin Fleischmann and I, over the past several years, have had related manuscripts returned by the editors without review from the *Journal of Electroanalytical Chemistry*, the *Journal of Physical Chemistry*, and various other refereed scientific journals. Editors of major scientific journals are censoring cold fusion manuscripts without any scientific review. This policy must change.[8]

But this was not the end of the matter with the *Electrochemical Society*. Before receiving Kohl's rejection letter of Jan. 12, 2002, Miles had, in fact, received an earlier letter from Roque J. Calvo, executive director of the *Electrochemical Society*, that stated, "Your manuscript has been received and is currently going through the review process." Along with the letter, Miles received a title page of his paper that had been stamped by *Electrochemical Society*, "For Review Purposes Only."

The subsequent refusal by Kohl to submit Miles' paper for review was too much to bear, as Miles advised Calvo in a March 11, 2002, letter:

I cannot, in good faith, continue my membership in a society that does not strictly adhere to principles of the scientific method with respect to peer-review of new, controversial concepts. ... Therefore please accept my resignation as a 35-year member of the Electrochemical Society and refund my dues and discontinue sending me the Journal of The Electrochemical Society. I am certain, as the years pass by, your rejection of this paper without peer review will be a black mark on your society.

It has been a tough road for Miles and his wife, Linda Miles. Miles has traveled the world in pursuit of opportunities to research cold fusion. When the funding for the Japanese New Hydrogen Energy program ran out, they moved back to the United States. With all the challenges he has faced, his interest in cold fusion has not wavered:

My own results convinced me that cold fusion was real. I always want to be on the side of TRUTH because this will eventually have to be accepted. However, for truth to win has taken much longer than I expected.

Close to retirement, at 67, Miles has never had any thoughts of giving up:

No, never. However, I regret my lack of funding for research in this area and the passage of years when I could have been contributing more to this field.[9]

Dr. Antonella De Ninno, an Italian nuclear physicist and fusion researcher with the Italian Agency for New Technology, Energy and Environment, is another persistent researcher. De Ninno stated in a September 2003 letter that three journals to which she submitted a scientific paper on cold fusion rejected it without even submitting it for a referee's scrutiny, despite the fact that the director of her facility, Nobel physics laureate Carlo Rubbia, believed her work was groundbreaking. A fourth journal replied to her, "This paper cannot be published neither here or elsewhere because it deals with a subject which has already proved to be false."[10]

The fact that cold fusion researchers repeatedly have proved initial criticisms wrong has escaped most conventional scientists, who figure that they would have read about any significant developments in cold fusion on the covers of the world's most prominent scientific journals.

While editors make the decision to approve or reject a paper for publication, they depend on the counsel of peer reviewers to guide them. If, as in the Oriani case with *Nature*, the two peer-reviewers advise against publication, the editor likely will follow such advice. In this way, the editors cannot truly be blamed for the continued neglect of cold fusion; the reviewers have much of the responsibility in suppressing news of developments in the field.

However, when an editor makes the decision not to send a paper out for review, the responsibility for halting progress in scientific research is in the hands of the editor. In a Jan. 9, 2004, rejection letter from Ian Osborne of *Science* magazine, Oriani provided an example of this polite yet maddening interference in scientific progress that pervades the field:

> Although your analysis is interesting, we feel that the scope and focus of your paper make it more appropriate for a more specialized journal. We are therefore notifying you so that you can seek publication elsewhere.

In fairness, even in the case in which editors dismiss the paper without review, can the full blame be placed on their shoulders? After dealing with the annoyance of conservative reviewers on the subject, it may seem pointless to send cold fusion papers out for review. These selected comments from "Reviewer #2" in Oriani's submission to *Nature* demonstrate the attitude of some reviewers:

> I, for one, am fed up with the confusion created by preliminary reports based on a small number of runs. Furthermore, the time for preliminary reports is past. Very preliminary "positive" reports have now been followed by very comprehensive "negative" reports, and the authors have to contend with this background and with the consequent extreme scepticism (disbelief!) [sic] that now exists. I feel that, for publication in a prestigious journal, authors of papers like this now have to meet a high standard of proof.

Between June 2001 and November 2001, Storms submitted, in series, a comprehensive "positive" report to four major science journals in an effort to bridge the communication gap between the cold fusion community and the general science community. All four journals rejected the paper. The response from Dr. George Bertsch, editor of *Modern Physics,* was representative of the problem: "Cold fusion is a classic example of pathological science, and I will certainly not publish articles supporting its disproven claims." [11]

Some scientists have made bitter and aggressive attempts to keep news of cold fusion progress from others. As Miles recalled, "a cold fusion session was planned for the Los Angeles American Chemical Society National Meeting in April of 1995. It created so much controversy that the oral session was cancelled."

Among his other battles to inform fellow scientists, Miles organized a cold fusion session for the 35th American Chemical Society Western Regional Meeting on Oct. 6-8, 1999, in Ontario, California. Notable participants in the session included Fleischmann, McKubre, John Dash (Portland State University), Stan Szpak, Robert Bush, Benjamin Bush (University of Texas), and Talbot Chubb, (retired, Naval Research Laboratory). The cold fusion sessions were eventually permitted, but they didn't happen without an uproar.

> The planned session created a huge controversy with other ACS members who threatened to resign from the American Chemical Society if the cold fusion session was allowed. In turn, my co-workers at China Lake, who were the organizers of this regional American Chemical Society meeting, stated that they would likewise resign from American Chemical Society if the planned cold fusion session were cancelled!

Miles, ever determined, was able to surreptitiously get his paper on the SPAWAR work presented at the Electrochemical Society meeting in San Francisco in 2001, only because "the organizers of my session were caught off-guard," he said. "They didn't realize it was about cold fusion; otherwise, they would have cancelled my paper."

CHAPTER SEVENTEEN

Silence and Neglect

"This sort of dwindling band of true believers each year gets together and talks about the wonderful progress that's been made. None of the rest of us can ever see that." [1]

-Dr. Robert L. Park, director of public information for the American Physical Society

Storms has responded to cynics like Park in this way: "Many people see only what they want to see. At some point in the history of any new idea, the problem no longer involves logic but is psychological." [2]

Having failed to find a suitable explanation for the revolutionary claims of cold fusion, critics invariably have resorted to the position that some unknown source of error must be at fault. They have clung to this argument beyond reason, even when their investigations have revealed no flaws. Ultimately, they have concluded that, while no flaws are evident, that can't mean that no flaws exist; there must be flaws, because the claims fly in the face of theory!

On request of the authors of this book, calorimetry specialist Lee Hansen of Brigham Young University, Utah (not to be confused with Wilford Hansen of Utah State University), an associate of physicist Steven Jones with Brigham Young University, reviewed a recent paper by McKubre. Without having had the benefit of a hands-on visit, Hansen commented, "It's really difficult to identify the source of an error just from a report like this, a written document." "It [cold fusion] is theoretically impossible," he stated.

Hansen was persuaded by his fixed belief in a non mutable theory and possibly by the fact that a student of his had unsuccessfully attempted to replicate a cold fusion experiment. This led to his conclusion:

> The fact of the matter is Pons & Fleischmann's experiment never did demonstrate any excess heat. ... It was nothing more than experimental error.[6]

Other skeptics have gone further than just to evaluate a cold fusion paper for errors. Some have visited a laboratory, examined the evidence first-hand, and scrutinized the experiment for errors. Still, none has been identified that could account for the excess heat effect.

Over two separate visits, in 1991 and 1993, five extremely high-profile scientists walked into one of the United States' top cold fusion laboratories, SRI International, for another look. They were hired to inspect the continuing cold fusion research and to convey their findings to the Pentagon and to an American industrial consortium, the Electric Power Research Institute.

These five scientists were not peripheral to the original controversy; rather, most were key figures in the public attack against cold fusion.

Two of the scientists were also members of a secretive U.S. organization known as the JASONS, a group of 50 scientists, primarily physicists, with whom the Pentagon and the U.S. Energy Department have consulted since 1959 on spending decisions for defense-related technologies. In October of 1993, JASONS chairman Richard Garwin and JASONS member Lewis performed an extensive, two-day evaluation of work performed by the staff of McKubre.

Garwin is one of the most prominent and well-respected physicists in the United States. His background includes appointment as the director of applied research at the IBM Thomas J. Watson Research Center, as well as membership in the IBM Corporate Technical Committee. He has been a professor of public policy in the Kennedy School of Government at Harvard University.

Garwin's work has included the design of nuclear weapons, instrumentation and electronics for research in nuclear and low-temperature physics. His list of achievements includes, among numerous others, publication of 500 papers. He has been granted 45 U.S. patents.

Garwin took a strong stance against the possibility of cold fusion. In 1989, he was quoted as saying the following to a Texas A&M University cold fusion scientist:

> The one thing [I know] for certain [is] that, if 10 volts are applied to the cell, no matter how one imagines a deuterium nucleus scooting around inside, it is never going to end up with more than 10 volts of energy. ...You are kidding yourself.[3]

Lewis, who was unable to see any unusual nuclear or chemical reactions in his own cold fusion attempt, was among the Caltech team at the 1989 science conferences who stood on chairs, commandeered microphones, shouted and denounced cold fusion.[4]

In their 1993 follow-up report to the Pentagon, Garwin and Lewis described their observations of data that supported the elusive and revolutionary cold fusion anomaly excess heat, though they dared not call it cold fusion, nor did they go so far as to claim that what they had observed was proof of cold fusion. The complete report can be found on the Web at www.newenergytimes.com. A few key excerpts from their historic report follow:

> Neither Nate Lewis nor I has any reluctance to entertain and recognize a purely experimental discovery. We don't need a theory to make us believe our eyes. But we do need a significant, reproducible effect, and that is what McKubre and his colleagues are attempting to produce. ...

> We held [a cold fusion cell] in our hands and are now quite familiar with its construction. We also had extensive discussions of data from one of these cells, which according to a summary chart has provided about 3 percent excess heat. This is not a derived kind of excess heat, related to the minimum electrochemical energy required to

135

electrolyze water to produce dihydrogen(g) and dioxygen(g), but an honestly phrased fractional excess over the total power delivered to the electrochemical cell itself. ...

The uncertainty in excess power measurement is about 50 milliwatts, but the excess power appears to be on the order of 500 milliwatts or even 1 watt peak [10:1 signal to noise ratio]. However, excess power is still a deduced quantity and depends upon the calibration of the calorimeter. [McKubre's closed-cell, mass-flow calorimeter features a 98 percent heat recovery and an absolute accuracy of $< \pm 0.4$ percent.]

On cells L3 and L4, we note that a chemical reaction involving the Pd at perhaps 1.5 eV per atom would correspond to about 3.5 kJ of heat; this is to be compared with the 3 Mj [one thousand times greater] of "excess heat" observed, so such an excess could not possibly be of chemical origin.

We believe that there are a few things (probably irrelevant) not very well understood by the experimenters.

While cells that do not "load" the requisite 0.92 D:Pd level would indeed serve as controls, we believe it highly desirable to run a number of cells on light water equal to the number of experimental cells.

This is a serious effort to obtain reliable calorimetric data on heavy water electrolyzed in a cell with a palladium cathode [that is, cold fusion cell]. It is larger in scale and has more electrochemical expertise than the work of Tom Droege of Fermilab, who obtains excellent data but no excess heat.

We have found no specific experimental artifact [error] responsible for the finding of excess heat, but we would like to see eventually (as would the experimenters) a larger effect and one that can be more reliably exhibited.[5]

Garwin and Lewis clearly said that they observed evidence of excess heat. Although the report lists various concerns and objections, they were noted to be inconsequential to the persistent and clear confirmations observed. Nevertheless, Garwin worded the conclusions ambiguously, thereby permitting either a supportive or unsupportive interpretation of the excess heat findings. So even though their observations corroborated the excess heat phenomenon, Garwin provided a politically safe, rather than an honestly conclusive, report.

Learning of the undisclosed Garwin and Lewis report years later, Fleischmann has found it in his heart to forgive and forget. In light of Lewis' recognition of the excess heat at the SRI International laboratory, Fleischmann reflected compassionately, perhaps gloating ever so slightly, "I forgive him. It must have been a bitter pill for him."[7]

In 1991, two years before the Garwin and Lewis visit, the Electric Power Research Institute (EPRI), the funding agency for SRI International's cold fusion research, hired three outside consultants eminently qualified in the related sciences.

This group included Dr. Charlie Barnes, a highly regarded nuclear physicist from Caltech, and two senior electrochemists, Dr. Howard Birnbaum of the University of Illinois and Dr. Alan Bard of the University of Texas. All were members of the 1989 U.S. Energy Department cold fusion panel which had rendered the historic decision against cold fusion.

Like Garwin and Lewis two years later, Bard privately yielded to the reality of what was before him in the SRI experiment, which he had publicly and ferociously rejected:

> In conclusion, the work at SRI to detect and understand excess-heat effects during electrolysis with [palladium] cathodes has been carried out carefully and has shown some excess heat effects that cannot readily be attributed to artifacts or errors.[8]

In the same report, Bard, apparently wishing to play down the historic findings of excess heat, honed in on its lack of theoretical justification at the time:

> The detection of nuclear products at levels consistent with the excess heat levels has not yet been accomplished. Such detection is

necessary before a convincing case can be made for a process involving a nuclear reaction.

As time and progress have marched on, so have Bard's ostrich-like comments. In 2004, when nuclear product and excess-heat correlation was clearly demonstrated, he devised a new argument to dismiss cold fusion:

> If [cold fusion researchers] are saying, "We are now able to reproduce our results," that's not good enough. But if they are saying, "We are getting 10 times as much heat out now, and we understand things," that would be interesting.[10]

Bard's comments demonstrate the dismissive attitude that has pervaded critics' approach to the phenomenon, even when first-hand observation takes place. Bard continually has raised the bar by setting arbitrary and unrealistic standards for acceptance of the phenomenon. This scientist is ignoring the fact that new scientific discoveries rarely arrive in a complete package, replete with a theory of understanding.

McKubre and Passell reported that Birnbaum and Barnes submitted reports comparable to that of Bard, confirming the SRI International cold fusion experiments without acknowledging their merit.[10]

McKubre said the EPRI administrators had privately hoped to break through the communication barrier between the cold fusion camp and the rest of the scientific community:

> We were, I guess, disappointed that "the three wise men," as we called them, chose just to write a report in accordance with their responsibility as consultants and nothing more.

> EPRI paid the three as consultants to see if they could find any reason why what we believed to be true wasn't true, and so we spent a lot of time informing them. I actually lectured for a whole day to these guys. It was the longest lecture I ever gave in my entire life.

The secret hope of the EPRI project managers was that they would be persuaded and convinced and would spread the seeds of knowledge among their peers, which they didn't. They simply took this as a consulting opportunity, to listen and learn but not say anything to anyone else. [11]

On making their observations, should Garwin, Bard and Birnbaum have taken further action to support cold fusion research? Their silence was hypocritical. Some would call it deplorable. Beaudette had this to say:

They were silent, completely silent. Were their individual reputations so important to them that they could not be put at risk by reporting publicly what they had found? What they had found was that McKubre's experiments did reveal the existence of anomalous power as far as these experts were able to tell. Their silence was unethical in view of the importance of the matter at hand and the special expertise the four could bring to bear on the subject. [12]

CHAPTER EIGHTEEN

Pathological Criticism

"The only thing pathological about cold fusion is the way the scientific establishment has treated it." [1]

- Sharon Begley, *The Wall Street Journal*

"Some years ago I discovered in the heavens many things that had not been seen before our own age. The novelty of these things, as well as some consequences which followed from them in contradiction to the physical notions commonly held among academic philosophers, stirred up against me no small number of professors - as if I had placed these things in the sky with my own hands in order to upset nature and overturn the sciences. ... Showing a greater fondness for their own opinions than for truth, they sought to deny and disprove the new things which, if they had cared to look for themselves, their own senses would have demonstrated to them."

- Galileo Galilei

The criticism of pathological science is one which has quite frequently been leveled at unusual investigations, which admittedly are often at fault. However, there is also the situation that people will criticize a field long after they should really have given up. And that is pathological criticism. They just get trapped in a situation, they have made a criticism and they have to maintain that criticism against all the evidence. [2]

- Martin Fleischmann

The oft-heard maxim "Extraordinary claims require extraordinary evidence" was coined by Marcello Truzzi and repeated by Carl Sagan, among others. Interestingly, according to a friend who knew Truzzi well, he reconsidered much later in his life and concluded that "the phrase was a non sequitur, meaningless and question begging, and he intended to write a debunking of his own words." The phrase is not a part of the scientific process; it is subjective and ill-defined.[3]

Opponents have used Truzzi's words as a barrier to deflect and dismiss the consideration of new and conflicting information. The claims of Fleischmann and Pons certainly were extraordinary, and to the angst and ire of the highly skeptical, the hard-to-believe announcement by the University of Utah was devoid of a mountain of evidence, as is the case with any new discovery. While such a basis for objection may have been justified, if unwise, 15 years ago, this is no longer the case. Continued dismissal based on the application of Truzzi's maxim is a blatant dereliction of duty.

The investigation behind this book included brief interviews with nearly every prominent cold fusion opponent. The intent was to obtain informed, balanced viewpoints.

It is helpful first to distinguish a few terms. Merriam-Webster's dictionary defines a critic as "one who expresses a reasoned opinion on any matter especially involving a judgment of its value, truth, righteousness, beauty, or technique."

A skeptic is one who adheres to "the doctrine that true knowledge or knowledge in a particular area is uncertain" and "the method of suspended judgment, systematic doubt."

A cynic is one who is "marked by an often ill-natured inclination to stress faults and raise objections" and "one who believes that human conduct is motivated wholly by self-interest."

William J. Beaty, an electrical engineer, computer programmer and webmaster, had this lively term and definition to offer:

"Pseudo-skepticism," a variety of pseudoscience: the behavior of highly biased "sneering scoffers" who try to legitimize their prejudice by donning the mantle of science and proper skepticism. They claim to support reason/logic while in fact filling their arguments with plenty of ad-hominem, straw-man, poisoning-the-well, and numerous other emotion-enflaming fallacies and debating tactics.

Beaty has written an excellent article titled "Symptoms of Pathological Skepticism," that goes into great depth on the subject.[4]

Rochus Boerner, while a Ph.D. candidate at Arizona State University, quoted Dr. Robert Wood, director of research and development for McDonnell-Douglas Astronautics Division, as saying, "Far more harm is done to the progress of science by skepticism than by gullibility." Boerner wrote his own astute article on the subject, "Notes on Skepticism," excerpted here:

> Many who loudly advertise themselves as *skeptics* are actually *disbelievers*. Properly, a *skeptic* is a *nonbeliever*, a person who refuses to jump to conclusions based on inconclusive evidence. A disbeliever, on the other hand, is characterized by an *a priori* belief that a certain idea is wrong and will not be swayed by any amount of empirical evidence to the contrary. Since disbelievers usually fancy themselves skeptics, I will follow Truzzi and call them *pseudoskeptics* and their opinions *pseudoskepticism*.[5]

A person who offers genuine critique and who is a proper skeptic offers value to society and science. These roles can be considered protectors of the integrity and credibility of science, as well as protectors of the public from that which is purported to be scientific but which inevitably is not.

The attitude of the most outspoken opponents is *cynicism*. This is unfortunate, because there are valuable and important roles that true critics and skeptics offer to society.

A reasoned opinion requires being informed and responding to the current body of knowledge. If one takes a reasonable look at cold fusion research and its adherence to the scientific method, one cannot fail to recognize the viability of this new science.

McKubre offered additional insights into the extraordinary resistance to the new idea of room temperature fusion:

> The barrier here, what we've been facing all of this time, and what is probably under recognized is, Why can't we convince these people that there's a real effect? And the problem is that knowledge brings responsibility. If they know there's a real effect, then they're obliged to do something about it. And none of them is willing to change what they are already doing and take on a new task or a new viewpoint. None of them is willing to face up to that responsibility. It's much, much easier to deny the knowledge.[6]

Rothwell, who has followed cold fusion from its beginning, thinks that a more down-to-earth, survival mechanism is underlying much of the resistance. It's a simple case of following the money. Writer Upton Sinclair aptly noted:

> It is difficult to get a man to understand something when his salary depends upon his not understanding it.

Rothwell remembered a conversation he once had with the Navy's Szpak:

> I once asked him why he thought scientists oppose cold fusion. "Is it," I asked, "because they are conservative or they cannot deal with new ideas or they do not want to learn new skills? Are they are in love with their own theories?" He said, "Nonsense, that stuff has nothing to do with it; scientists believe whatever you pay them to believe."

Szpaks' comment is obviously a generalization that doesn't apply to all scientists but does illustrate the point. If cold fusion research were broadly funded, scientists in every academic, military and commercial environment most likely would be engaged in the work.

Rothwell sees that cold fusion has the potential to upset a long-standing balance of power in academic research:

Cold fusion calls for knowledge of materials, electrochemistry and solid-state physics. Plasma fusion researchers who build Tokamaks do not have such skills, or they do not have them in any greater abundance than people in other academic departments do. So in 1989 they concluded - correctly, I think - that if cold fusion began to succeed, it would soon be funded out of their budget, but they would not get the contracts.[7]

Many critics contend that, in order to achieve credibility, cold fusion must be verified by people whom they consider to be reputable, mainstream scientists. This is, in fact, an inane and biased position, because many cold fusion researchers have been involved with conventional science and even, in some cases, hot fusion research for two or three decades! The caliber of these researchers is what one would expect from any mainstream, reputable scientist. Most proceeded quite cautiously before identifying themselves with cold fusion. McKubre of SRI International, for example, reports that only after a full year's research did he become convinced that the field of cold fusion constituted a legitimate scientific endeavor.

Nevertheless, it has been challenging for cold fusion researchers to obtain the cooperation of scientists in the nuclear physics community to scrutinize their work. Storms described his view of this challenge in a November 2003 telephone conversation:

> The problem is to find a person who is respected by conventional science who will take the time to learn what is known and then discuss this with objectivity. Most mainstream scientists are woefully ignorant of the field because they do not take the time to study a subject they either believe - or have been told - is nonsense.[8]

Several cold fusion scientists, including McKubre and Storms, recounted rejected attempts to hand-deliver scientific papers to Dr. Robert Park, the director of public information for the American Physical Society. "Park has always made a point of refusing to look at printed papers about cold fusion." Rothwell said. "He will not touch them, literally. When I tried to give him one by McKubre, he let it drop on the floor rather than touch it." [9]

MIT physics Professor Herman Feshbach was an ardent foe of cold fusion. When handed cold fusion papers for his review, he gave this bombastic response:

> I've had 50 years of experience in nuclear physics, and I know what is possible and what is not. I'm not going to read it. It's all junk.[10]

Walter Gratzer is a professor of chemistry at the University of London. He criticized cold fusion in his 2000 book, *The Undergrowth of Science: Delusion, Self-Deception, and Human Frailty*.[11] In a November 2003 e-mail, he admitted that he more or less blindly repeated what other critics had said on the topic:

> I gave cold fusion as an example of what has been called "pathological science." I have to say that it is not my field. ... What I wrote in the book was based on my reading at the time, which convinced me that the cold fusion uproar was based on atrociously bad science by people stampeded into hasty experiments and premature publication, ... but I do not think it is for outsiders like myself to pronounce judgments. ... I think you should consult genuine experts on nuclear reactions.[12]

He offered as big names Lewis, Koonin, Bard, Garwin, William Happer, Jacob Bigeleisen at State University of New York, Stony Brook, Frank Close (Exeter College, Oxford), and David Williams.[13]

Robert Park has repeatedly dodged inquiries about the reasons for his continuing rejection of evidence for cold fusion. An American Physical Society member reported that he personally invited Park to attend the 2003 10th International Conference on Cold Fusion, but Park declined, saying that he had to spend time writing his weekly e-mail column, instead. One of the authors of this book interviewed Park as follows:

> Park: "They have one each year, this sort of dwindling band of true believers. Each year they get together and talk about the wonderful progress that's been made, and none of the rest of us can ever see that."

146

Krivit: "Which papers do you know about?"

Park: "Well, let me give you the experts: Steve Koonin at Caltech, and he has a colleague in the Chemistry Department, Nathan Lewis."

Krivit: "But you, yourself, are there any particular papers you can recommend ... perhaps showing claims of neutrons or helium? Are there any papers that you're familiar with?"

Park: "Golly, I haven't gone through that in so long. I don't know offhand what to recommend."

Krivit: "What do you think about the Tokamak?"

Park: "It turned out to be much harder than we thought, but they make steady progress. It's not spectacular progress, but the joke is it's the energy source of the future and it always will be, because they're constantly giving you an estimate of how many years before we have controlled fusion reactors in business and it doesn't happen."

Krivit: "In an Internet newsgroup, somebody asserted that you wouldn't even read a single cold fusion paper."

Park: "Oh, no, I read them till I was sick of them. There's a lot of paranoia in that group, and I don't know how to account for it."

Krivit: "So there's nothing new that you've heard of that is meaningful in the last few years out of this cold fusion group?"

Park: "No, They never use the word cold fusion anymore. Its low energy nuclear reactions."

Krivit: "Is there anything you're aware of written within the last five or 10 years?"

Park: "Nothing really. ..." [14]

Following the trail of experts named by Park and Gratzer, inquiries were directed to Koonin and Lewis of Caltech. Each was asked whether they could comment on recent developments in the field.

In a January 2004 e-mail, Koonin stated that he was unaware of any recent facts pertaining to cold fusion.[15] This reply was surprising considering that he is regarded as an expert.

Lewis, another so-called expert, had this to say:

> I've been out of that area for a decade or so. Consequently, I have no basis for commenting on anything that has happened in that period of time sciencewise.[16]

William Happer, who will be remembered for his pompous "incompetent boobs" remark, professed in a January 2004 e-mail that he was current on developments in the field of cold fusion.

> Happer: "I do follow these activities with interest. ... There continue to be papers published and claims made. None that I have seen look credible."
>
> Krivit: "Would it be possible for you to point out some of these papers?"
>
> Happer: "Well, if you want the complete archive from a 'true believer,' you might want to contact Bob Bass."
>
> Krivit: "I'd prefer if you could identify a few of the papers to me yourself. Would that be possible?"
>
> [Several hours later]
>
> Happer: "I am still looking around for some good articles on alleged recent advances in cold fusion to refer you to. That I am having a hard time is symptomatic of the problem that community has." [17]

How was it that Happer was able to follow the activities with interest but was unable to cite or lay his hands on a single paper?

A "Google" search of "cold fusion papers" immediately brings Rothwell and Storms' www.lenr-canr.org cold fusion library to the top of the list. As of 2004, the free and voluntarily operated library lists a bibliography of 3,000 cold fusion papers and makes 350 papers available for direct download from the site.

Bass, it should be noted, is a Rhodes scholar and, as mentioned earlier, a theoretical physicist who formerly worked in the Princeton Plasma Physics Laboratory. In 1980 and 1984, he was awarded two U.S. patents in optimal hot fusion reactor design, which are discussed as promising ideas in three books on controlled thermonuclear fusion power. Bass has worked in the aerospace industry on automatic flight controls, launch vehicles, spacecraft, and missiles, as well as target tracking systems using a variety of sensors, including radar and infra-red. He is known internationally for his work in these areas and served as the chairman of one of the sessions at the first International Federation of Automatic Control conference in Moscow, in 1960. He is also licensed to practice intellectual property law before the U.S. Patent and Trademark Office and is a registered patent agent.

Bass held an appointment as a professor of physics and astronomy at Brigham Young University for 10 years. His background includes employment as a senior scientist at Hughes Aircraft Company, associate professor of aerospace engineering sciences at the University of Colorado, chief scientist in the Advanced Systems Group at Litton Industries and a post at the Rockwell Science Center. As well, his curriculum vita lists numerous honors.

Despite appearing ignorant about current facts pertaining to cold fusion, Happer displayed no hesitation in denigrating the recent efforts of the U.S. Department of Energy to re-evaluate cold fusion (details at the end of Chapter 19):

> "I think a review is a waste of time," said Happer, who was a member of the [first Department of Energy cold fusion review panel in 1989] and the former head of the Department of Energy's Office of Energy Research (now the Office of Science). "But if you put

together a credible committee, you can try to put the issue to bed for some time," he added cynically.[18]

Next on the expert list were the United Kingdom's Dr. Frank Close, author of the 1991 exposé, *Too Hot to Handle: The Race for Cold Fusion,*[19] and Dr. David Williams,[20] who led Harwell's team on its Fleischmann-Pons replication study. Of the past decade in cold fusion research, each said that he had heard nothing of substance. Close offered the following reason for ignoring developments in cold fusion:

> Nobody in mainstream science is putting serious research time into this. ... When someone produces hard evidence, then I'll get interested. But I've been saying that for 15 years now.[21]

When one of the authors of this book asked for his definition of "hard evidence," Close defined it as "evidence that is reproducible under varied conditions ... performed rigorously." This criticism will be shown in Part Three to have been answered satisfactorily by the numerous studies performed over the past 15 years. It is therefore an inexcusable justification for the continued neglect of cold fusion.

When asked to define a "mainstream scientist," Close said that any "scientists in universities" can offer "sound opinions." [22] In fact, two dozen university scientists were interviewed or cited for this book. (See Appendix A.)

The notion that there is a lack of mainstream scientists putting serious research time into cold fusion is a myth. So is the notion that cold fusion's vocal opponents of the past are or were ever truly qualified for the title of expert in this new scientific field. Their original appointment by the scientific establishment as experts was in fact misguided.

One retired professor who has seen much more than his share of derision is John O'M. Bockris, whose complex and dramatic story will be told in forthcoming chapters. This chapter concludes with several excerpts from his paper, "Accountability and Academic Freedom - The Battle Concerning Research on Cold Fusion at Texas A&M University," published in the journal *Accountability in Research* in 2000:

Scientists within their time have always thought that what they know is "the final truth." They do not understand the temporary nature of the theoretical construct. Hence, a man whose proposal does not simply add and support the theoretical constructs of the time will not be approved but will, in fact, be ridiculed and rejected. His funding will rapidly sink.

At present, the attitude toward paradigm-inconsistent findings is automatically to reject them, with anger, insisting that they are due to sloppy experiments or fraud. That is dangerous, for it may keep alive a horse which should be led out to pasture. Science is a changing, developing body. The key to progress is to find experimental anomalies to the present view and to investigate them.

The advancement of the science of cold fusion calls for curious people to return to observation and interpretation, the predecessors of the philosophies and beliefs that compose our current understanding of nature.

From there, the scientific process, a tried and true method of discerning nature's truths, does its job. Observation, hypothesis, experimentation, control groups, replication, publication of results, and eventually accepted theories are the accepted and proven modalities for the discerning scientist.

The role of the honest skeptic is essential to the progress of science. Through skepticism, we sort the wheat from the chaff and fact from fantasy. When the sorting is done, and done well, we are left with a very strong sense of what is gold and what is garbage.

CHAPTER NINETEEN

Fifteen Years of Progress

"The problems of the skeptics are their problems. I measured excess heat and nuclear products ... with 100 percent reproducibility." [1]

- Dr. Alexander Karabut, Specialist in Heat Physics, Nuclear Rocket Engines, and Nuclear Material Science at the LUCH Association at Podolsk, Russia,

"It is evident from the [research] presented that cold fusion is going to bounce back as a fascinating new area of nuclear science." [2]

- M. Srinivasan, Associate Director, Physics Group, Bhabha Atomic Research Centre (BARC), Trombay, Mumbai, India, (retired)

Over the past decade, cold fusion researchers have developed a love-hate relationship with their ostracism from mainstream science. While some enjoy the anonymity, all gladly would welcome adequate funding and broader scrutiny of their experiments. In view of their exclusion from many academic venues, cold fusion researchers have developed an ethic of constructive criticism toward one another's work. While this does not take the place of more widespread publishing and peer review, after 15 years of focused study of the anomalies in metal deuterides and hydrides, the analysis of cold fusion has become so specialized that few outside of the community would even qualify as knowledgeable peers.

Nagel explained the challenges of this new field to a public audience at the August 2003, 10th International Conference on Cold Fusion:

> This so-called simple cold fusion cell is a sophisticated experiment that requires real expertise. ... This field is intrinsically interdisciplinary. It requires knowledge of physics, chemistry, electrochemistry, nuclear physics; electrical, mechanical and thermal engineering, instrumentation science and technology, solid-state physics, chemistry materials science, statistics and data analysis.[3]

In a potential sign of changing times, in 2003 several cold fusion experimenters gave well-received presentations at meetings of the American Physical Society and the American Nuclear Society. Some nuclear physicists who strongly criticized cold fusion in the past have begun to express support for the field. Dr. Lowell Wood, a prominent physicist with the Lawrence Livermore National Laboratory and former protégé of Edward Teller, cautiously has been taking note of the developments:

> The claims of the cold fusion community are undeniably exceptional, and the experimental results supporting such claims must withstand exceptional scrutiny in order to be taken seriously. Thus far, ... no single example of them does so - though some already come close, and I wouldn't be surprised if one or more of them eventually does.[4]

Nagel disagrees with Wood and says that cold fusion has arrived: "There are many individual studies where the data is essentially bulletproof. The collection of them is very, very compelling."

Because of numerous challenges, "many of the early experiments were deficient," Nagel said. Many discontinued the work because of perplexing inconsistencies:

> Investigators who stayed with the problem in the early 1990s realized the complexity involved and systematically addressed the needs of the experiments. Hence, the quality of the experiments and the results increased with time. For the past 10 years, the precision and accuracy of cold fusion experimentation has been very good, with experimental errors many times smaller than the observed excess powers in many cases.[5]

Renewed Interest

In 2001, Dr. Frank E. Gordon, head of the Navigation and Applied Sciences Department of the Space and Naval Warfare Systems Center, San Diego, of the United States Navy wrote in the forward to "A Decade of Research at Navy Laboratories":

> We do not know if cold fusion will be the answer to future energy needs, but we do know the existence of the cold fusion phenomenon through repeated observations by scientists throughout the world. It is time that this phenomenon be investigated so that we can reap whatever benefits accrue from additional scientific understanding.[6]

Recently, the U.S. Department of Energy began to re-assess its opinion of cold fusion. On Nov. 6, 2003, Hagelstein of MIT, McKubre of SRI International, Nagel of The George Washington University, and Randy Hekman of Hekman Industries met with the U.S. Department of Energy's Office of Science to request a new U.S. government review of cold fusion research. On July 16, 2004, one of these cold fusion representatives commented, "The hope is for a conclusion that says there are indeed anomalous effects, which deserve study."

Throughout much of 2004, Nagel has spoken to various U.S. government and military agencies. As he told the 70 participants at a January 2004 Department of Defense workshop, "it is highly likely that your perceptions of the cold fusion field are (a) out of date and (b) wrong."[7] Inevitably, his confrontational statement raises eyebrows; yet it becomes clear from his presentation that this is, in fact, the case.

Fifteen years ago, the panel of scientists consulted by the Department of Energy to review cold fusion research closed the book on the discovery just eight months after Fleischmann and Pons had announced it to the world. Not only did panel members miss many available facts at the time, but they also overlooked the potential for future gains in scientific knowledge. More compelling cold fusion data began emerging shortly after the 1989 panel completed its task, and a great deal of experimental information was acquired in the 1990s.

154

News of the Department of Energy's renewed interest first appeared in March 2004 in a short article written by journalist Bennett Daviss in the British journal *New Scientist*. Though no press release was issued, Department of Energy spokeswoman Jacqueline Johnson confirmed in a telephone conversation on March 17, 2004, that the department had begun laying the groundwork for a second review of cold fusion. The object of the review was simply to determine whether cold fusion represents genuine science. Presumably, if a positive outcome were to occur, federal funds would be granted for cold fusion research. Considering the overwhelmingly negative impact of the original review, the mere fact of cold fusion receiving a second chance is a stunning reversal.

Mallove, in an interview by Kenneth Chang of *The New York Times*, exclaimed, "I am absolutely delighted that the Department of Energy is finally going to do the right thing. There can be no other conclusion than a major new window has opened on physics." [8]

The 2004 review was structured far differently from its 1989 predecessor. Rather than an outside panel's leading and managing the review, it was fully organized and directed by Department of Energy staff. This approach appears to be a more effective and less politically motivated evaluation of the new science.

The Department of Energy staff initially conferred by phone with the four cold fusion representatives to acquire knowledge of the status of cold fusion research and to develop a plan by which the Department of Energy could perform its assessment. Energy Department staff expressed a willingness to evaluate a circumscribed area of the cold fusion field: the experimental results of the palladium/deuterium work. The staff excluded theoretical research, experimental work with palladium/hydrogen and transmutation research.

The Department of Energy requested that the four cold fusion representatives write and present a summary paper and select six published papers representing important studies in the field. The completed summary paper contained references to 130 cold fusion papers. In an Aug. 3, 2004, e-mail, one of the four cold fusion representatives expressed frustration at the daunting task of selecting only six papers from the 3,000 known cold fusion papers.

> Because of the time limitation (and the very diverse opinion set in this very young field), we were not able to accommodate the full breadth of good results or opinions. We were also constrained by the Department of Energy to a closed review, and we will abide by their process.

These documents were sent out for review to two dozen scientists in various U.S. government laboratories and universities. Half of these reviewers submitted written reports to the Department of Energy sometime before Aug. 23, 2004, on which date the other half met face-to-face with the Department of Energy staff and cold fusion community representatives.

The all-day meeting took place at a hotel in Rockville, Maryland, and was the only such group meeting to occur over the course of this review. Reviewers heard presentations from Dr. Steven Jones, Dr. Vittorio Violante (Agency for New Technology, Energy and Environment, Italy) and Andrei Lipson (Russian Academy of Sciences and visiting professor at the University of Illinois, Urbana), among others.

One of the cold fusion representatives remarked that the various rounds of group and private discussions held during the daylong review were well-planned and effective and that they reflected a sincere and refreshingly honest discussion. The review marked a potential landmark for bridging a 15-year communication gap between the cold fusion community and the general science community.

The Department of Energy's Office of Science staff requested individual reports to be submitted within a few weeks by the reviewers who attended the meeting. An extensive report, like the one written in the 1989 cold fusion review, was not expected. "The hope is that there will be a short one- to two-sentence summary from the Department of Energy within about a month after the review," one representative wrote to a fellow cold fusion researcher.

As this book goes to press, the question is, Will reviewers and Department of Energy staff acknowledge the mountain of evidence in support of cold fusion, or will political interests derail the field's overdue recognition? The field of cold fusion, and potentially this planet's future, could take a historic turn. Alternatively, it could continue plodding along on meager funds until this generation of cold fusion pioneers has died.

Part Three

DISCOVERIES AND MYSTERIES

CHAPTER TWENTY

Objections Overturned

In 1989, many of the stewards of nuclear science, the nuclear physicists, felt certain that the explanation for cold fusion must be laboratory error. The claims of table-top nuclear energy were inconceivable in view of half a century of established theory and hot fusion experimentation. The physicists raised four main objections: the standards for reproducibility were not met; the usual evidence for nuclear reactions (neutrons and gamma rays) was absent; available techniques for measuring excess heat were unreliable; and theoretical understanding was incomplete.

The key to understanding the controversy and its outcome is this: the nuclear physicists' unstated objective was to explain the phenomenon away, while the discoverers' aim was to explain its existence. Those who panned the discovery were content to end their inquiry there. Those who pursued cold fusion research were eager to explore its nature and potential.

Much has transpired over the last 15 years in the science of cold fusion. The primary objections have been overturned, and fascinating new discoveries have taken place.

Today, many researchers indicate that cold fusion is highly reproducible. The basic claims of nuclear-scale energy without nuclear radiation have been substantiated hundreds of times over. Scientists around the world have replicated the effect repeatedly (Figure 3-1), and they have demonstrated it using a variety of experimental methods.[1] The supposedly lacking nuclear products, which originally prompted critics to dismiss cold fusion's founders as delusional, have been measured convincingly.[2]

A common myth about cold fusion is that a single key will make it work. To the contrary, the subject matter is infinitely variable and complex; its success depends on a multitude of incremental insights and understandings, rather than one "Eureka"! moment. While many of these triumphs appear only as abstruse readouts on diagnostic equipment, dozens of important advances have indeed occurred, and many pieces of the puzzle have been found.

Certainly, had researchers gained the initial support of the scientific establishment, progress would have been much greater by now. Perhaps cold fusion-powered generators would have arrived. Nevertheless, with only modest resources available to them, scientists around the world have made impressive headway in their understanding of this burgeoning new field of science. No longer is there a question of whether cold fusion is real, or even *if* it works. Scientists are improving their understanding of *how* and *why* it works. The greatest remaining mystery is, Can cold fusion be scaled up to provide for civilization's needs for electricity and heat?

Through a confidential survey of cold fusion researchers who attended the August 2003 10th International Conference on Cold Fusion (Figure 3-1), the authors of this book learned that research continues in at least 13 countries. While far more researchers undoubtedly are working than are represented by this survey, these numbers portray a continuing worldwide effort. Among survey respondents, 73 researchers work in university laboratories, 53 in government and military laboratories and 49 in private industry.

In the United States, although many work in military or university settings, the lack of government funding has meant that quite a few cold fusion researchers have resorted to setting up their own private laboratories. Many have devoted their retirement years to solving the mysteries of cold fusion.

Worldwide Cold Fusion Research

Number of Researchers Known to Be Studying
Cold Fusion By Country and Setting
Data collected August 2003 at
the 10th International Conference on Cold Fusion

COUNTRIES	RESEARCHERS			
	University	Military	Nonmilitary	Private
Australia	1			1
China	14			
Denmark			1	
England				1
France				3
Israel				12
Italy	4		19	8
Japan	27			3
Korea	1			
Romania	1			
Russia	3		19	
Ukraine	1		3	
USA	21	11	3	21
Totals	73	11	42	49

LABORATORIES		U.S.	Non-U.S.
Universities		13	21
Nonmilitary Government		3	16
Military		3	

Figure 3-1. Worldwide Cold Fusion Research (August 2003)

163

CHAPTER TWENTY-ONE

Reproducibility

At the outset, cold fusion was extremely challenging to reproduce. To establish a new scientific phenomenon, scientists typically aim for a completely repeatable experiment. The physicists who criticized cold fusion indicated that, if it were genuine, the phenomenological effect would succeed every time an experiment ran.

But as Charles Beaudette noted in a September 2004 telephone conversation, 100 percent reproducibility is not always required or reasonable to expect. A good example of that is "Dolly," the cloned sheep. Dolly resulted only after hundreds of tries. Even so, when the cloning was announced in February 1997, it was accepted overwhelmingly as being a result of science, despite the fact that it did not have a repeatable experiment.

In 1994, Michael McKubre explained an important distinction about the challenges of reproducing cold fusion:

> The issue of reproducibility, or its lack, has been frequently misunderstood in this field. The difficulty has been in reproducing the conditions which produce the results, not reproducing the results. [We find that], if we meet the conditions that we have established, then we, in every case, produce excess heat.[1]

Beaudette notes another perspective that has hindered full reproducibility, "The atomic structure of the [palladium] cathode cannot be repeated because mankind does not know how to do that."

Failure may result from any number of aspects of the experimental conditions, such as impurities in the sample or subtle variations in the experimental method. Dr. Francisco Scaramuzzi, one of Italy's most respected physicists who has extensive experience in both hot and cold fusion, has disagreed with critics who argued that low reproducibility legitimized the rejection of cold fusion. Scaramuzzi explained.

> It is not correct to state, as many have done for cold fusion, that non-reproducibility necessarily means a wrong experiment. A new field, at its beginning, is often characterized by lack of reproducibility, and it is the task of the scientists operating in that field to understand what is going on, in order to pursue reproducibility. This has been done in the case of cold fusion, making meaningful, even though slow, progress.[2]

Scaramuzzi was one of the first to pioneer a new method, which used deuterium gas, in the form of D_2, in contrast to the electrolytic method, which uses deuterium in the liquid state as a component of heavy water for cold fusion experimentation. McKubre explained the benefits of this method:

> The first thing is that there are fewer moving parts. It doesn't require special skills and knowledge. Very few people have the specialized training with the electrolytic methods to make them work. [The deuterium gas experiment] does have its own tricks; for example, you have to take very good care and pay attention in preparing the surfaces of the samples, but basically it is a much easier experiment to do.[3]

Initially, cold fusion experiments achieved excess heat less than 10 percent of the time. By 1991, scientists made important strides in their ability to reproduce the Fleischmann-Pons effect. As researchers improved their understanding of the subtle properties of palladium, they learned that different batches from the same manufacturer varied in their capacity to host the excess-heat effect. While some samples resisted cracking, many were vulnerable to developing microscopic cracks in the palladium as the deuterium loaded into it. This defeated the palladium's capacity to retain deuterium at high enough concentrations; subsequently, the excess power effect did not appear.

166

As did many other researchers, Fleischmann and Pons began using silver-palladium alloys, instead. The alloys resisted cracking; however, according to Ed Storms, "the silver prevents significant amounts of deuterium from going in, so you solve one problem, but you create another." Storms now bypasses this problem by laying down either thin films or micro particles of palladium, which "prevents stress from concentrating in one area and allows the entire sample of palladium to expand."[4]

Systematic experimentation resulted in several additional insights regarding what was needed for a successful experiment. First, the excess power effect requires that the "loading," that is, the ratio of deuterium atoms to palladium atoms, be above a certain threshold. The electrical current density also must surpass a threshold, one which varies widely from one experiment to another. A third key parameter that researchers discovered was the need to take care to prevent normal water from being present with the laboratory-grade heavy water.[5] The inadvertent contamination of a heavy water cold fusion cell by normal water, even by humidity in the air, could inhibit the cold fusion effect.

Before 1989, McKubre had worked with palladium and deuterium electrolytic cells, but not for cold fusion. His prior work provided an immediate advantage when he started his own Fleischmann-Pons replication. Still, the materials in the cold fusion experiment behaved in a very odd manner.

"For example," McKubre said, "if you take a palladium wire and you snip it into 10 equal lengths, set up 10 identical experiments with 10 identical cells, every one of the experiments will give different results and will require different parameters to attain the excess heat effect. It was a surprise to me because I had been performing electrolysis with palladium and deuterium for 10 years before 1989, and I never expected this huge degree of variability. It is profound. It was nearly inconceivable to me that such hidden variables could exist and cause such drastic variation on cells' reproducibility."

One researcher who brought great insight into the metallurgical aspects of palladium was Vittorio Violante, McKubre said. "In the early 1990s, Violante discovered that there were certain metallurgical constraints and that there were ways of treating the palladium that would make it much more reliable in terms of the loading and heat production."[6] Formally trained in

167

chemical engineering, his career focused entirely on hot fusion until 1989. McKubre, who is familiar with Violante's work, said, "Vittorio has been recognized for his highly innovative work in the field and is officially sanctioned by an Italian government agency similar to the U.S. Department of Energy, to perform cold fusion research.

The fourth discovery was that to exercise control over the start of the excess-heat effect, in Nagel's words, "you have to shock the system in some fashion."[7] Originally, hundreds of hours went by before scientists would notice excess heat. Dennis Letts, a researcher in Austin, Texas, provided a simple but profound breakthrough:

> It is commonly believed that a lot of vibrational activity occurs on the surface of the palladium cathode, that the surface is alive with activity. I made some calculations and found that there might be some vibration on the cathode that would match the frequency of a laser. I had no specific reason to think that it would trigger any excess heat, but I tried it just for fun.[8]

To Letts' great surprise, he saw the temperature readout of the cell jump up, and he observed excess heat develop in historic time, less than five minutes. Letts explained, "There appears to be a resonance effect." He and his partner, Dennis Cravens of Cloudcroft, New Mexico, refined the technique and introduced the "Letts-Cravens Effect" in 2003 at the 10th International Conference on Cold Fusion, in Cambridge, Massachusetts.

The Dennises initially had the awkward problem of both responding when others attempted to address one of them. By applying some of their creative ingenuity, they quickly overcame this dilemma. Speaking of Letts, Cravens said with a wide, toothy grin, "he's called D1 because he's *much* older than I am." Cravens speaks in a rich, Southern twang, in contrast to the smooth-spoken, stylish Austin, Texas, Letts. Cravens loves science, and his enthusiasm and animated gestures show it. A most inventive fellow, he jests that he could make batteries from fruit, and a flashlight from carbonized bamboo - if he were ever to be stranded on a deserted island.

The two were great fun during the 10th International Conference on Cold Fusion. A crowd huddled around their laptop, which was connected through the Internet to their Texas laboratory. On one screen, a webcam displayed an active cold fusion cell, while a second screen showed its calorimetry readings.

Cravens pointed out that "input power in watts is down here," referring to a steady horizontal blue line across the screen. As Letts turned on the 30 milliwatt laser by remote control, Cravens directed the crowd's attention to the red line on the graph, the output power. The red line, for the most part, appeared somewhat like a bell curve. It started low, peaked, and then came back down. "When the input from the laser was applied, the excess power jumped 300 milliwatts, a tenfold increase," Cravens said.

This effect reportedly was replicated by laboratories in California, New Mexico and New Hampshire.[9] Researchers have used other means of jump-starting the cold fusion experiments, as well.

With the current understanding, Nagel said, "there is an equation available that allows us to predict the excess power if we know the thresholds for the current density, for the loading, and the time variation of the loading. That's substantial progress." [10]

As a result of many such discoveries in recent years, the rate of reproducibility of cold fusion experiments has increased significantly. Antonella De Ninno said in an October 2003 e-mail, "We have improved our techniques year after year, and we now know why an experiment does or does not work. Our experiments in recent years are now about 75 percent successful, up from about 40 percent five years ago." [11]

The authors of *The Rebirth of Cold Fusion* conducted a survey (Figure 3-2) of researchers who attended the 10th International Conference on Cold Fusion. The primary objective was to ascertain the average rate of reproducibility for experiments showing excess energy or nuclear products. Of 43 researchers whose e-mail addresses were publicly available, 24 chose to participate in the survey. Ten respondents answered the questions on reproducibility.

The success rate of cold fusion experiments within the prior 12 months was 83 percent. This was up from 45 percent five years ago. Impressively, within batches of palladium previously shown to be effective, several researchers claimed a *100 percent* rate of success. Dr. Emilio Del Guidice, physicist and senior scientist with the National Institute for Nuclear Physics in Milan, Italy, wrote in a September 2003 e-mail, "In our experiments, we successfully observed cold fusion every time that we were able to attain the proper loading ratio."[12]

Figure 3-2. Cold Fusion Reproducibility (2003)

Cold Fusion Reproducibility (Figure 3-2)

From a November, 2003 survey of 10 respondents

Researcher's Nationality	Field of Degree	Years of Cold Fusion Research	Years of Hot Fusion Research	Estimated Number of Experiments Performed	Reproducibility Rate 5 Years Ago	Reproducibility Rate Last 12 Months	Do You Conclude That Nuclear Activity is Occurring?
Italy	Chem. Engr.	na	yes	na	na	50	na
Russia	Condensed Matter Physics	18	na	1,000	na	60	Yes
Italy	Physics	14	16	300	40	75	Yes
United States	Mass Communications	13	no	6,000	25	75	Yes
United States	Phys. Chem.	14	no	200	10	80	Yes
United States	Metallurgy	14	no	3,000	50	90	Na
Japan	Nucl. Engr.	14	20	20	70	100	Yes
Romania	Atomic Physics	10	no	40	70	100	Yes
United States	Radiochemistry	14	no	700	50	100	Yes
Russia	Nucl. Rocket Engr.	13	2	3,500	na	100	Yes
TOTAL ESTIMATED EXPERIMENTS				14,720			
AVERAGE REPORTED REPRODUCIBILITY					45%	83%	

Excess Heat Replications

The basic claim, that low-energy nuclear reactions produce more energy (in the form of heat) than they consume, has been demonstrated repeatedly in numerous experiments, laboratories and countries around the world. In 1998, Storms identified "over 50 studies reporting repeated examples of excess energy production, ... most of which have been published at least in conference proceedings." [13]

Adding to the validity of this new science are the handful of methods by which cold fusion has been demonstrated.[14] Of course, having a variety of approaches also has made the process of replication more challenging, because all cold fusion scientists cannot possibly develop the skills or have the time to pursue knowledge of all the various methods. The replication of experiments is therefore an area which remains underdeveloped.

"[Replication] is a very complicated issue," Nagel commented. "Variables such as current density, loading density, equipment, materials geometry and materials sources can vary immensely, ... but there's been a lot of progress made on that front." [15]

At SRI International, for example, McKubre's team developed a first-principles, state-of-the-art mass-flow calorimeter (Figure 3-3) for the sole purpose of measuring excess heat from cold fusion experiments. He discussed this in a 2002 interview on radio station KUER:

> We know how to measure heat very accurately now. Here at SRI alone, we probably spent half a million dollars developing a highly accurate, highly sensitive calorimeter that was stable for long periods of time.

172

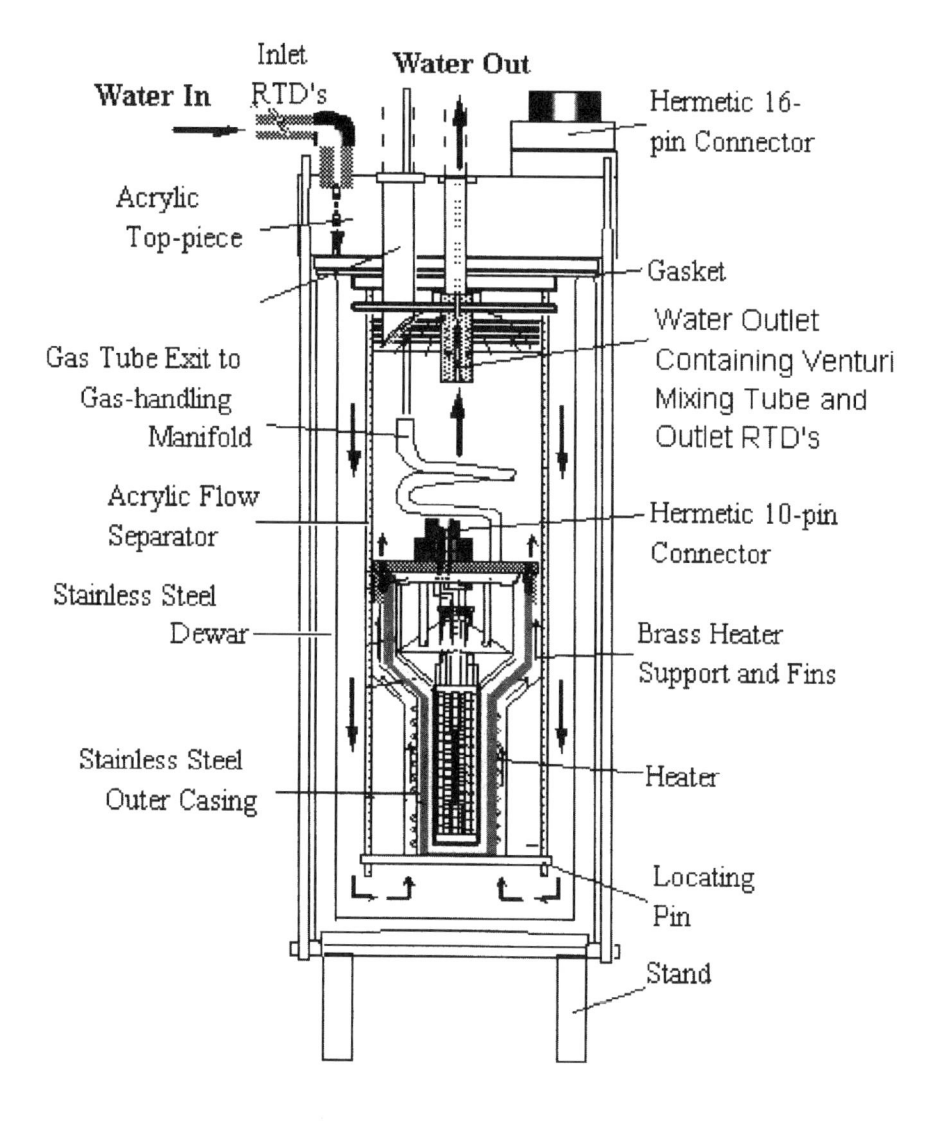

Figure 3-3. SRI International Calorimeter

McKubre noted that, although they have measured heat at 90 times the measurement uncertainty (90 sigma), the data is not accepted by many physicists. The physics community, according to Beaudette, has taken the position that "mankind does not know how to measure heat." "Paradoxically," McKubre said, "in the world of physics, experimental evidence is often accepted if it's as little as three times the measurement uncertainty."

CHAPTER TWENTY-TWO

Nuclear Evidence: Tritium

Cold fusion research initially drew strong skepticism from the scientific community for its failure to demonstrate evidence of neutrons and tritium, the dominant nuclear byproducts of hot fusion.

Over time, researchers learned that, because of the differences in the experimental environment between cold and hot fusion (as well as the different nuclear process involved), different byproducts are to be expected. In cold fusion, Nagel said, "Neutrons are rare. Tritium is much more common, though still not in enough quantity to account for the heat measured in the [cold fusion] calorimetry experiments according to hot fusion theory."[1]

A key distinction between hot fusion and cold fusion is the microscopic environment in which the cold fusion reaction is thought to occur. Known as the "lattice," this environment is the arrangement of atoms within an element, in this case, palladium. The atoms appear as an ordered array, somewhat like the cross-hatched pattern of a trellis or garden fence, in a three-dimensional configuration.

McKubre, who spent a solid six years of his career pursuing the nuclear products in cold fusion, discussed his finding during a Nov. 27, 2002, KUER interview with Douglas Fubbrezio:

> It turns out that the nuclear products are helium-4, helium-3, and tritium, which are the products of fusion. I use the phrase "cold fusion" now. I didn't use it two or three years ago because I wasn't

certain what the effect was. I thought it was unreasonable to assert a mechanism when you had no proof of that mechanism. Now, we have adequate proof that the mechanism is a fusion reaction. I know with certainty that we have a nuclear effect that produces heat and fusion products. We're entitled to use the phrase "cold fusion."

[The effects are] probably even more general [than just fusion]. I think the fact is, and it is an exciting fact, nuclear effects can be influenced when they occur in a crystalline body [metal]. The fact that these nuclear effects occur inside the crystalline palladium lattice very much changes the rates of the reactions and the distributions of the products. The nuclear reactions that people are claiming are not restricted to fusion. They encompass a wide range of nuclear effects.

A Tritium Tutorial

Shortly after the cold fusion discovery was announced on March 23, 1989, numerous laboratories around the world reported the evolution of tritium from the palladium-deuterium experiment. The researchers who reported tritium included Bockris, Howard Menlove, Storms, Talcott and Tom Claytor, all with Los Alamos National Laboratory and Daniele Gozzi with the University of Rome, Italy. A team led by Mahadeva Srinivasan at the Bhabha Atomic Research Centre in India also observed tritium. Srinivasan recalls their discovery:

> Within two to three weeks, we got our first results. And several groups got excess heat, but the most important and unbelievable phenomenon at that time was the observation of tritium.[2]

While tritium was observed in very small quantities in only a few cold fusion experiments, its discovery was a historic event for the validation of the field. At least, it would have been, were the results believed and accepted at the time. Whereas neutron emissions from cold fusion experiments were elusive and marginally above background level, tritium provided hard evidence that, indeed, nuclear reactions were occurring in these tabletop chemistry experiments.

Storms offered a brief tutorial on the subject of tritium:

> Tritium normally exists as a gas and is an isotope of hydrogen. In all of its chemical properties, it's just like hydrogen but with some small differences because it has a different mass. Tritium is also radioactive.
>
> The presence of tritium is not natural because half of it decays away every 12.3 years. So any significant amount of tritium that's on earth has to result from some man-made event, like atomic bomb tests - or cold fusion.

Tritium can't be detected with a Geiger counter because its level of radioactivity is too weak, Storms said. He explained how tritium is measured from a sealed container:

> We extract a small amount of fluid from the cell using a hypodermic needle, which is passed through the lid in the top of the cell. This fluid is then mixed with a scintillation fluid. Scintillation fluid is an organic compound that gives off light when a [radioactive] particle generated by the decaying tritium passes through it. Next, the mixture is placed in a machine that can detect the small amounts of generated light. The number of light flashes is measured over a known interval of time. Because the decay rate of tritium is known very well, the amount of tritium required to cause the observed number of light flashes can then be calculated.[3]

Tritium Discovered at Los Alamos

Los Alamos is the birthplace of the first atomic bomb and was the home of the top-secret World War II Manhattan Project. This laboratory and its staff have a long, experienced history researching tritium, among other nuclear weapons research programs. In one of the most thorough early investigations, Storms, Talcott, Menlove and others dedicated themselves to the search for tritium production in cold fusion experiments.

Storms and Talcott's group ran "fifty-three electrolytic cells of various configurations and electrode compositions" and found "significant tritium in

11 cells at levels between 1.5 and 80 times the starting concentration after enrichment corrections are made." They noted that, "although the amount of tritium made in this study is small, it is well outside of the uncertainty in the measurement, up to 785 times the standard deviation based on a total of all random errors." Their study took into account "consideration for errors based on chemiluminescence, contamination, or the product of enrichment from normal electrolysis."[4]

Storms explained that the tritium work was the first indication to him that cold fusion was real:

> We established, using a number of different techniques, that this tritium could not have come from any other source except from a nuclear reaction within the cells.

> When a person sees the process happen and finds no error, that's pretty doggone good proof that it's real. Because it was real, I didn't want to do anything else. But then the U.S. government put the brakes on future studies, and work in the United States almost stopped. However, it did not stop in other countries. Thanks to work done elsewhere, the field is slowly being accepted in the United States.[5]

Tritium Discovered by Bockris at Texas A&M

No accounting of the history of cold fusion would be complete without an introduction to John Bockris. Famous as well as infamous, Bockris was second only to Fleischmann and Pons in attracting media attention in the early days of cold fusion research. His story may well be the most complex and misunderstood story in all of cold fusion's history. An entire book could be filled just with the cold fusion-related adventures and misadventures at Texas A&M.

Born in Johannesburg, South Africa, in 1923, Bockris earned his bachelor's degree in chemistry at the University of London in 1943 and his Ph.D. at London's Imperial College in 1945, at 22. At 23, he began teaching as a lecturer at Imperial and was responsible for leading a group of 10 graduate students.

Bockris is retired from his most recent appointment, at Texas A&M University as a Distinguished Professor in chemistry. Before that, he was chair of physical chemistry at Flinders University in South Australia, and before that, he was appointed professor of physical chemistry at the University of Pennsylvania. In the 1960s, he led the largest electrochemical research group in the Western Hemisphere.

Bockris' background and academic achievements are voluminous and include 750 scientific papers, a dozen books, and several commonly used college texts, among them his best-known book, *Modern Electrochemistry,* written with A.K. Reddy and published in 1970.

One graduate student who immensely enjoyed Bockris' lectures at Imperial College was none other than Martin Fleischmann, who was two years behind Bockris at the school. Although he was unable to squeeze into Bockris' full load of graduate students, Fleischmann found it irresistible to attend Bockris' groups and participate in after-school social activities with the more senior graduate students.

In the very serious-looking photograph in Figure 3-4, the lads are pulling a prank in honor of All Hallow's Eve, a holiday which is the United Kingdom's version of Halloween. The contraption in the photo, dubbed "The Geister-Phone," purportedly was able to tune in to the voices of ghosts from the spirit world. Bockris is at the far right of the photo, with Fleischmann just behind him and to Bockris' right.

Figure 3-4. The Geister Phone

Bockris enjoyed Fleischmann's company. He recalled with amusement that Fleischmann developed a unique way to encourage uninvited visitors in Bockris' office who had overstayed their welcome, to leave: he would write complex calculations on the blackboard. Most electrochemists were no match for Fleischmann's unusual proficiency at mathematics and would announce shortly thereafter that they had to be on their way, rather than face an embarrassing showdown with a junior student.

Bockris recounts the initial cold fusion news, carried on television:

> I heard about it the day after "The McNeil/Lehrer Hour," but I did not see the show. I said to myself, "Oh, my God, that damn Martin Fleischmann!" You see, because I know Martin rather well and, um, [Bockris hesitates] I have to be very careful about what I say because I'm being recorded and you're probably going to put it in your book … well, he's a very brilliant guy. There's no doubt about that. Let me make that very clear. But he has certain drawbacks. One is that of

being "wooly." If you asked Martin a question, instead of saying "yes" or "no," he will say, "What a good question, John! That's something we really ought to discuss." Or, "That's a gas!" – a favorite thing he used to say. He'd go on and on and on, and you'd never get your question answered. So that's "being wooly."

But he's such a clever, inventive fellow with so much to give that I always took the attitude that, for God's sake, let's preserve this boy. I call him a boy, and he's two years younger than I.

So when I heard about this the next day, I called Martin. Martin at this time was being called about 10 times a minute, and he had to shut off the phone. But when he knew it was me, it was different. We had been friends for years, so he accepted my call.

Bockris recalls asking Fleischmann for details about the experiment. He remembers his answer clearly:

You go along at low current density for many hours, and then you jack it up! – 10 times, 100 times more current density, and then it happens!

As we found out later, that's not enough information, because the "go on for a long time" is a *very, very long time,* 500 hours or so. That is the essence of it, and then you see the [excess] heat.

Also, I asked Martin another question, which was, "How did you get the lithium hydroxide?" He told me that he had got it by putting lithium [a soft metal] in the solution and letting it dissolve to form lithium hydroxide. Those were the two bits of information that he gave me, and in that sense, I had a flying start, with all my graduate students [at Texas A&M]. I had 20 of them [working with me] at the time." [6]

Bockris, who was regarded as one of the world's top electrochemists, suffered a major political setback because of his pursuit of cold fusion, and especially his reports of tritium. Bockris claims that his group at Texas A&M was the first to observe tritium in cold fusion experiments.

As a scientist, Bockris has demonstrated consistently excellent integrity. Personally, few would regard him as a modest man. Beyond his pursuit of the highly controversial discovery of cold fusion, Bockris' overly confident and daring proposals in the realm of scientific experimentation, coupled with a lack of social and political deference, ignited hostility and doubt about his professional integrity. On two occasions, Bockris was charged with misconduct by his peers and was formally investigated by the Texas A&M administration. In both cases, investigations found no evidence to substantiate the allegations. Even though he was fully exonerated, this information never made the news, and his reputation remains tarnished.

In the view of Tom Passell, "Bockris can't be faulted beyond the fact that he tries things that most scientists would never be willing to try." Passell is a nuclear chemist who earned his degree while studying at the University of California, Berkeley, under Dr. Glenn T. Seaborg. Together with several program managers who worked for the Electric Power Research Institute, he oversaw the Texas A&M cold fusion research, which also was funded by the U.S. Naval Research Laboratory and by the CIA.[7] Passel provided the following assessment:

His extensive series of textbooks about electrochemistry is a solid contribution and highly regarded in that field, so he has a long history of conservative research that does not shake up accepted paradigms. Yet he doesn't mind taking risks to explore the world. Even some cold fusion researchers blanche at some of his ideas. Often, his proposals have been off-the-wall.

When Bockris gets into his salesman mode, he loses that conservative image. In a way, you could say some physicists have launched into that speculative salesman mode by pushing the nearly impossible task of hot fusion. So I forgive him for such forays as his attempt to convert mercury to gold using a thermite reaction, or trying to see if transmutation could occur in a carbon arc under water. These last two go well beyond what I found even remotely scientifically possible or worth trying to sell. However, his work on tritium in electrochemical cells I found within the realm of possibility and worthy of being defended.

I personally like him and think he made a positive contribution to the field. His critics can readily use his more outlandish ideas to try to discredit him and [unsuccessfully] attempt to do such things as to strip him of his academic title at Texas A&M. [8]

Figure 3-5. John O'Mara Bockris

As did many other scientists around the world, Bockris expected that it would be just a matter of weeks before his team would observe excess heat produced by their experiment. Bockris and his staff worked feverishly, night and day, to achieve what they thought would be a relatively easy replication of the discovery:

I organized a group of three. We worked eight hours each for 24-hour periods for about six weeks. We worked on many things, and then we looked for tritium.

The first time tritium was detected in our group came as a surprise. At this time, both Charles Martin and his co-workers, and my own co-workers, were taking our solutions (after electrolysis) to the

Nuclear Engineering Department, because it was there that tritium-measuring capabilities were available. We had already made some half-dozen visits without seeing any tritium, and then [on April 24] 1989, the [surprised] technician who made the measurements exclaimed, "What have you done to this one?" He reported a very tritium-active cell for which a graduate student, Nigel Packham, along with others, had been responsible.

We took the solutions allegedly containing tritium to be measured at other places (outside Texas A&M), in particular to Los Alamos, and it was confirmed ... that it was indeed tritium that we had produced. The tritium in the electrolyzed solution was also confirmed at the General Motors Technical Center. The first published work was in the *Journal of Electroanalytical Chemistry* and [was] the earliest result published in a refereed journal.[9]

We found that, by working these cells of Fleischmann and Pons' that contained lithium hydroxide and deuterium oxide, we could produce this tritium in [relatively] great abundance, let's say, 10,000 times more than ought to be there, as it were. And let me stress that we couldn't do it every time, but about one result in five or in four, and eventually we worked up to two results in three, we could produce tritium.[10]

Unfortunately, science journalists and the world's media in general were not to know of the tremendous achievement of tritium evidence until many years later, because news of the early findings was pre-empted by a vicious and slanderous article by Gary Taubes, published in *Science* magazine.

Taubes Trashes Tritium

Bockris' priorities differed from those of others who were researching cold fusion. This did little to win him friends, even inside the cold fusion community, as Storms recalled:

John called me shortly after they had seen tritium and asked how my attempts were going. I told him, confidentially as one scientist to another, that I had several cells that indicated tritium production, but we still had much work to do. He promptly told the press that we also had seen tritium, which supported his claims. I soon received a call from a reporter asking about our work, which got me in considerable trouble at Los Alamos. The lab did not like people reporting their results to the press, especially in this subject. John was more interested in getting credit for being first than in being sure the observation was correct. This attitude seemed to be common at that time. Los Alamos did not play that game.[11]

Bockris' quest for attention drew to him a reporter, Gary Taubes, who was convinced not only that cold fusion was a worldwide blunder but also that some individuals were deliberately conspiring to produce false results. Mallove recalled being interview by Taubes:

> Taubes was very aggressive in his pursuit of what he thought was true, that fraud at Texas A&M played a major role in keeping cold fusion alive. He had traveled to the university, collected over 50 hours of taped interviews, and had zeroed in on one or more possible tritium-adulterers. He had become deeply involved in an investigation of their personal lives in an effort to come up with a motive; in one case, he even traveled to England in search of details on the suspect's family life. Taubes was focusing on personal factors that may have led a certain graduate student into deliberate tritium tampering. This is the hallmark of skepticism run amok that has pervaded the entire cold fusion episode.[12]

On June 12, 1990, Taubes, writing for *Science* magazine, launched a historic media attack against cold fusion. A press release titled "Cold Fusion Revisited" proclaimed the following:

> According to an investigative news report in the 15 June issue of *Science*, "suspicions were raised almost from the first that the tritium in the A&M cells was put there by human hands." Was this a fusion reaction, was it inadvertent contamination, or was it something more insidious?

Bockris submitted a rebuttal shortly after the *Science* magazine article ran, but the publication declined to print it. The following is an excerpt of the rejected letter followed by highlights from other documents:

185

It all began when Taubes came into my room one day, unannounced, without knocking. He's a great big chap; he looks like a football player. He was very nice and pleasant, and he was claiming he was a journalist. He wanted to write a book on cold fusion and wanted to know all about my results. I responded correspondingly; I showed him my notebooks and papers. He went away, and nothing happened, as far as I knew. But, in fact, lots of things were happening.[13]

Apparently, Mr. Taubes made a second visit to our university, but I knew nothing of this. Later on, it appeared that he had gotten a lot of information including confidential letters and memoranda which I had exchanged with Dean Fackler. How Taubes obtained these memos is not at the present time known.[14]

Then, about three months later, he came back again to my office. Now he was a changed man, extremely aggressive, and he was openly nasty.[15]

He said that he intended to attack cold fusion and to prove the work we had done was fraudulent![16]

He started off by an amazing two-hour confrontation with my graduate student, Nigel Packham. ... Taubes accused him of spiking the [cold fusion cell] with tritium from a tracer-tritium solution as the basis for our successful cold fusion experiment. The only evidence for cold fusion [in the world], he averred, was the work of [my group at] Texas A&M on tritium, and this tritium work [must have] been faked by the graduate student to get a fast Ph.D. [He alleged that] we would never have seen any tritium except for the fact that Packham actually put it in the cells!!! [17]

I said, "Look, we're completely free and open here. Go and sit with Nigel Packham alone in his office, have a microphone there and ask him any question you want to." I remained calm and told [Packham] that all we can do is to show him our lab books and tell him the truth. What he does with the truth is his conscience and his journalism.[18]

186

Packham recalled some warning signs that trouble was on its way before Taubes arrived:

> I was told of Gary's [forthcoming] visit, but I was also informed that it wasn't going to be a very pleasant visit, in that his message that he was going to bring to me was not one of belief in cold fusion but one of disbelief, because it went against all the natural laws of physics. It was much more going to be an aggressive interview about potential tampering of cells at Texas A&M University.
>
> When Gary was on the record with the cassette running, he was actually fairly jovial, fairly approachable. Nothing that he said was very intimidating, nor did it have any implication involved in it. However, about 45 minutes into our discussion, he asked whether we could turn the cassette recorder off. I did tell him that at that point anything that I was going to say, I would certainly not mind being repeated anywhere or being quoted. After some going backward and forward, I said, "Okay, let's turn it off." It was then that the completely different side, ... Gary's intimidation, came out.[19]

Bockris recalled Packham's exasperated response after leaving the interview with Taubes:

> He rushed into my room and said, "This man wants blood!"[20] Taubes had threatened Packham with a publication in the next day's *New York Times* reporting that his discovery of tritium was a fraud. If Packham confessed the fraud at the interview, he could avoid the article and perhaps find a job in Albania before the book Taubes was writing about the work came to be published.
>
> Nigel Packham told me that he asked the journalist what else he could do but report the facts as he had found them. The experiment did not always work, but when it worked, the results were unmistakably strong.[21]

Russ George, chief scientist of Saturna Technologies and a specialist in both hot and cold fusion, expressed the opinion that "Taubes was just plain dishonest." George said he was "a real *National Enquirer* personality ... no care whatsoever for facts."[22]

Bockris shared his own thoughts about Taubes' "witch hunt":

> Taubes' profession was two things. He wrote books about scientists, and he tried to denigrate them.[23] He has a history of writing books which are aggressively and negatively worded descriptions of famous professors. For example, he has attacked [Italian physicist and] Nobel laureate [Carlo] Rubbia in this way.[24] But he also wrote the text of novels in Hollywood. This is very remunerative. If you can get a job doing that, you've got several hundred thousand dollars a year. And he did this alternatively: six months writing in Hollywood, six months writing about scientists.
>
> Well, he was on the novel thing at this time. He wanted to make a big novel about cold fusion, and what's the point about making a novel about cold fusion if you just tell the facts? You've got to have some zip in it! Right? You've got to have something that makes people say, "Augghh!!" He wanted to have a fraud. He wanted to have a sensation, a disaster. That's how I see it.[25]

Taubes received assistance from an inside man at Texas A&M, Professor Kevin Wolf, a prominent nuclear chemist who conducted research in nuclear physics at the Cyclotron Institute at A&M. Wolf collaborated with Taubes to concoct a theory on how the tritium findings in Bockris' laboratory were not only artifacts but also fraudulently produced.

Wolf originally participated with Bockris' team on some of the cold fusion research that found tritium. He also performed his own research, which showed supportive evidence of tritium findings. At some point, for reasons on which one can only speculate, Wolf engaged in a broad campaign to distance himself from cold fusion. Some cold fusion researchers suspect that Wolf may have felt pressure from the nuclear physics community to preserve the status quo rather than break new ground in science.

Bockris reported that, on June 4, 1990, in a interdepartmental Texas A&M meeting, Wolf announced to all who had been working on cold fusion that *Science* magazine would be coming out shortly with an article that was very damaging to the Texas A&M chemistry department, and to Bockris in particular. The article, Wolf said, would explain that he was retracting his claims of tritium findings in his cold fusion experiments. Bockris reported that Wolf also announced at this meeting that the *Science* article would identify both Wolf's and Bockris' tritium findings as artifacts.[26]

Three days later, Wolf was featured in a *Wall Street Journal* article[27] in which he publicly retracted his supporting evidence of cold fusion. This came as a sigh of relief to the physics community which, until that point, had faced a severe political problem in that one of their most eminent members, Wolf, had supported the possibility of cold fusion. If tritium was just an artifact, on the other hand, then so was cold fusion, and the threats to prevailing science and hot fusion would vanish. In a one-two punch, Wolf simultaneously provided reasons to dismiss both his own tritium findings and Bockris': he alleged that the Bockris group findings resulted from the cell being spiked with tritiated water from a laboratory reference sample.

Wolf asserted that his own findings of tritium resulted from tritium impurities in the palladium. This theory later was disproved by Dr. Fritz Will, formerly president of the Electrochemical Society.[28]

The assertions by Taubes and Wolf in the June 15, 1990, *Science* article that the Bockris' tritium findings were artifacts made little sense to Los Alamos scientists. They proved that Wolf's concocted theories were also all wet. Storms, then at Los Alamos, stated the following in a letter to the editor of *Science* on June 25, 1990:

> The accusation made by Gary Taubes that cold fusion cells at Texas A&M University were "spiked" with tritium can be easily tested. It is not even necessary to trust the people at Texas A&M or Mr. Taubes. All that is required is to add tritium to an electrolytic cell and see if it behaves like the tritium claimed to be produced from cold fusion. This has been done [at Los Alamos], and the results show that the tritium claimed to result from cold fusion cannot be caused, at least in some cases, by the addition of tritiated water. I sent the results described herein to Gary Taubes on April 9, 1990, [two months] before his article was published. Unfortunately, he chose to ignore this information.

A few days after the *Science* story was published, Bockris sent the magazine a note in which he stated the following:

The fair thing, of course, would have been [for Taubes] to write an article and for *Science* to send it to me and ask for comments. Then the editors could have decided to publish or not publish as they felt fit and with the use of other referees. In fact, nothing of this sort was done. So this, of course, was *unethical* and *unfair* and something which no decent magazine would ever do. It is also extremely damaging in respect to myself, my graduate student, and my university.

Now to the matter of fraud. This is very easy to answer in one sense. Unbeknown to Taubes, people have been getting tritium right, left and center. I enclose a partial list of the laboratories at which tritium had been obtained. But, of course, the idea that Taubes had, [that] we were the only boys on the block who had got it, has been blown to pieces, and, therefore, the pressure to explain the Bockris results is now passé. So much then for the spiking. It didn't occur.[29]

In a subsequent letter, Bockris asked these questions of the *Science* editor:

What was the purpose, then, of *Science* employing a journalist who is also a Hollywood screenwriter and a past contributor to Playboy to write a gossip-based account which, by strong innuendo, suggests that a graduate student faked results of some of the observations made here? And why publish such a damaging account without first asking evaluatory comment on its contents by those directly concerned?[30]

As much as he felt surprised by the journalist's and publisher's behavior, Bockris was even more shocked and disappointed by the reaction of colleagues at the university and in the scientific community who acted as if he were guilty. He explained that, when the *Science* article ran, few people bothered to ask simple questions:

Every adviser knows his co-workers; I don't think that it is very likely that any of mine would do such a horribly dishonest thing. Why would they do it? Fifteen times?? For what purpose? With the danger of total ruin as a scientist upon discovery?[31]

Finally, in September 1991, Bockris and has team created a cell which evolved tritium for long periods. Bockris was thrilled that he might be able to show his colleagues the tritium results as they were occurring, yet, to his dismay, none cared to look:

> During the long period (about one month) in which [the cell] evolved tritium, I invited several colleagues in the Department of Chemistry to come see a result so unexpected, so anomalous within the chemistry of 1991. One said that his son had a birthday party that day so that he could not come to see the remarkable experiment, and the other said that he was going to Germany to do some experiments in an institute there. I asked two other professors, telling them that, by staying with the cell for one hour, they could themselves use the scintillation equipment in the next room and become convinced that the tritium concentration in the solution was increasing without [as suggested by Taubes] the means of the addition of tritiated water by stealthy secret nightly visits by graduate student Packham. These two individuals also declined to come and see, which reminded me of Galileo and the cardinals who, in the 16th century, would not look through his telescope, because it showed an irregular mountainous moon, although at this time the moon was supposed to be, in the Ptolemaic view of the church, "Queen of Heaven" and "perfect."

> On the other hand, when looked at psychosocially, rather than in terms of the spirit of scientific exploration, the attitude of these professors, as careerists rather than scientists, was rational. They had read the Taubes article in *Science*, they knew the production of tritium in the cold (according to current texts) was impossible, and they clearly preferred the quiet life rather than having to face a result which they could not explain and which would, in fact, put into doubt the basis on which billions of dollars [for hot fusion] was being spent.[32]

The media attention and fallout from the *Science* article took its toll on Packham, as well. At the time, Packham was finishing his Ph.D. thesis. It was a time of utter chaos for him. Normally, a thesis defense consists of a private meeting with committee members and perhaps a few additional attendees. Not this time. Because of the spotlight placed on him by Taubes' *Science* article, Packham's thesis defense was attended by several hundred

191

spectators and members of the press. To top it off, his wife was two days away from giving birth to their first child.

Packham, who now works for NASA in Houston, summarized his experience at Texas A&M University:

It was traumatic. But if, in hindsight, I knew what I was going to go through, would I do it again? Knowing the character it developed in me, yes, I probably would. I think I grew a lot. If Texas A&M had been the only group out there that said that they could produce excess heat effects, that would have been very different from the fact that there were people from, literally, all around the world - India, Japan - that were saying that they, too, were seeing something. Could they explain it? No. Did they necessarily need to at that point? In my opinion, and I think John would echo this, probably not. There are many things in this world that have unexplained reasoning behind them, and some of them are curious enough to investigate, and some will create a lot of problems.

Regarding Bockris, Packham added:

Bockris is a character. A lot of people don't understand him; a lot of people certainly don't like him. That's not John's fault. John does have some radical ideas, but sometimes radical ideas are the ones that move this crazy world we have along. [33]

Because of the pervasive misinformation spread by Taubes and *Science*, Bockris has lived these last 15 years with a tarnished reputation. Bockris contemplated whether to sue the magazine for defamation:

I took advice from seven different authorities on this issue. [The majority opinion] was that a suit would be impossibly expensive for me but of trivial financial concern to the publisher of Taubes' book and that what was really at stake was my scientific reputation. The only thing would be to wait and see. Would other people be able to replicate the results? If so, all would be well. If not, no suit would help.

This seemed good advice at the time; .... however, Taubes' article in *Science* spread throughout the world. The hundred independent replications of our original tritium work were known only to the few hundred researchers in the field.[34]

The June 12, 1990, *Science* "Cold Fusion Revisited" press release stated the following:

Through a series of exclusive in-depth interviews, *Science* reports on the events that amount to a case study in "the damage that can be done when questions of fraud, legitimately raised, are not seriously addressed by researchers or their institutions." The news article raises "crucial questions about how rumors and allegations of fraud should be investigated while ensuring academic freedom and protecting the reputations of scientists whose careers may be at stake."

The staff of *Science* magazine apparently believed that they were acting as guardians for the integrity of science; in fact, they violated their own professional integrity by reporting untruths and by causing harm to the subjects of their stories.

Bockris' rebuttal illuminated the political underbelly of science:

I think that the issue here in respect to the *Science* article is, How far do you go in publishing an investigative journalist's account of his gathering of gossip that a graduate student has been spiking solutions with tritium?

The allegations made are perhaps what a number of physicists would like as a solution to the puzzle of the anomalous behavior in Pd/D_2O. Because they were not addressed to the several hundred people who have taken part in experiments giving positive results on cold fusion but were focused on me and Nigel Packham, it is difficult not to sense a political element, clothed in talk of fraud and government investigation. Its publication wasn't good science. What the chairman of the board of directors of *Science* now has to decide is, Who takes the responsibility for the decision to publish such material, and was that decision truly good for *Science*?[35]

Miley, editor of *Fusion Technology* journal for 20 years, reflected on the matter:

> Normally, we'd say someone's innocent until proven guilty, and you'd be given the opportunity to have a trial rather than having an article written about what you've done wrong and identifying you as being guilty in the press rather than due process. All these things were happening, and it just makes one sad.[36]

It may eventually come to light that the damage from the Taubes' *Science* article suppressed the truth of cold fusion and delayed its progress. If cold fusion does, in fact, turn out to be a significant answer to the world's energy problems, then the delay in recognizing tritium as nuclear evidence of cold fusion will be considered highly unfortunate.

Mike Epstein, an assistant professor in the department of science at Mount Saint Mary's College, adapted the Lizzie Borden playground song to express his views of this regrettable chapter in scientific journalism:

> Gary Taubes took an axe
> Gave Pons and Fleischmann forty whacks
> And when he saw what he had done
> He gave John Bockris forty-one.[37]

CHAPTER TWENTY-THREE

Helium-4, a Harmless Byproduct

In the early 1990s, cold fusion researchers achieved a landmark finding that dispensed with another major concern of skeptics. They found that the quantities of helium-4 measured in cold fusion consistently correlated with the measurement of excess heat. In one of Storms' cold fusion review papers, he wrote the following:

> Helium was recognized early in the field's history as being a likely nuclear product, but its difficult detection had to await the careful work of Miles et al. .... In each case, care was taken to eliminate helium that might enter the cell from surrounding air. However, not all attempts to detect helium have been successful, partly because excess energy is difficult to produce and partly because measuring small amounts of helium in deuterium is difficult.[1]

At least five scientific papers have reported quantitative relationships between heat and helium-4. Two of these studies were conducted in the United States, two in Italy, and one in Japan.[2-8]

In Italy, Scaramuzzi led a major effort to pursue nuclear evidence. A number of other Italian researchers continued his pioneering work in the measurement of helium from cold fusion experiments, including Daniele Gozzi (Department of Chemistry, University of Rome), Tullio Bressani (Department of Experimental Physics, University of Tornino), Antonella De Ninno and Vittorio Violante.

Early on, signs had been present that helium-4 might supply the missing nuclear evidence required to establish the authenticity of nuclear reactions at low temperature. But helium-4 is particularly difficult to measure accurately at the low power levels at which most cold fusion experiments run.

Consequently, ordinary instrumentation is inadequate to observe it. Because helium is not radioactive, one cannot use a radioactivity detector. Helium has a mass nearly identical to a deuterium molecule, which rules out the use of normal mass spectrometers. Rothwell wrote that the amounts of helium generated in typical cold fusion experiments are "fantastically small" samples to measure. Furthermore, Rothwell said, "helium contamination is ubiquitous; it will slowly permeate glass, rubber, and plastic." He stated, "Miles has pointed out that a 1-watt fusion reaction would take 73,000 years to produce a single mole (4 grams) of helium. There are two rules when attempting to detect helium: use stainless steel flasks and tubing to prevent permeation, and second, use a very high-resolution mass spectrometer to distinguish between helium and deuterium gas." [9]

While some cold fusion experiments have indeed run at high power levels, so far they are the exception. This point seems to have been either ignored or misunderstood by the most vocal opponents of cold fusion. For example, Frank Close, speaking emphatically to correspondent Jerry Thompson on a 1994 Canadian Broadcasting Corporation "Prime Time News" special explained his perspective:

> There is not a single experiment that has claimed to produce the nuclear products that would be required, given the process that Fleischmann and Pons claimed that they were reporting in 1989.
>
> Originally the claims were "nuclear process," and everybody said, "Where's all the radiation?" It was very quickly clear that there was no radiation about. Now, to mainstream scientists, that said, "There isn't [any effect]." We were convinced that that was definitive evidence that there isn't anything. So then, those who wished to believe that there was something said, "Ah, well, maybe there are unknown mechanisms that *hide* the radiation." Well, I don't believe a word of that! But let's, to be devil's advocate, stay with that for a moment. So the radiation doesn't come out. Something must be left behind, and I invented the name "nuclear ash" for that.

So, if it were the case that nuclear products were found at the level of billions for every watt and if there are claims that there are hundreds of watts for tens of minutes, there's [got to be] many, many billions of nuclear products that should be around. Those amounts are *trivial* to find for a nuclear scientist. It's like having thunder flash in front of your face and trying to hear it. It's that easy. The fact that those things have been looked for and not found are, for me, the *evidence that they are not there.*

Nevertheless, not all physicists in 1994 had as much trouble as Frank Close in hearing the thunder flash. Jean Pierre Vigier, a theoretical physicist from the University of Paris, who was the editor of the highly respected *Physics Letters* journal, pursued what may be considered a more rigorous course of skepticism. Rather than seeking reasons why cold fusion couldn't be possible, he studied the literature in depth and performed his own experiments, as he explained to CBC's Jerry Thompson:

> In the beginning, I didn't believe in it! When I saw the explanation, I said this must be some artifact in the experiment or measuring device of Pons and Fleischmann. I didn't believe it because the nuclear ashes were not there. But then, our experiment got excess energy, so unless you want to refuse to "look into the telescope," you have to accept that. And second, [there was] the growing evidence in favor of an energy produced by hydrogen. ... Now we know that, if you shoot very high energy, a few hundred thousand amperes in a hundred nanoseconds, then you get huge fluxes of neutrons which do come from fusion reactions.

But testing the helium-4 hypothesis took time. As Rothwell wrote, "Miles began research on helium detection in 1990, in collaboration with Benjamin F. Bush and J.J. Lagowski at the University of Texas. Bush is an expert in dealing with contamination from air, a critical factor in this experiment." In three studies, samples of the effluent gas from the experiment were analyzed at three laboratories. Positive results of helium evolution from Miles' first experiment during 1990-1991 were verified by the University of Texas. Both his 1991-1992 study, analyzed by Rockwell, and his 1993-1994 study, analyzed by the U.S. Bureau of Mines in Amarillo, Texas, offered further corroboration of the helium evidence.[10]

Nuclear evidence also was found by the team at SRI International when they performed a painstaking five-step process to measure helium in their experiments. As McKubre noted in a November 1998 *Wired* magazine interview, "First, we check for helium in the instrument, then the helium background in ambient air, then the helium being generated by the apparatus. Then, we check the air again, and then we check the instrument again."

Figure 3-6 shows a set of the SRI team's helium-4 measurements. Values for the active cell as well as a control cell are shown. The air from both was evacuated before starting the run, as evidenced by the starting point near zero parts per million. The control cell, using hydrogen, shows a signal that remains relatively unchanged as time increases. Around Day 15, the active cell surpassed the known ambient level of helium-4 (5.22 ppm) and continued upward to near 11 ppm before decreasing slightly.

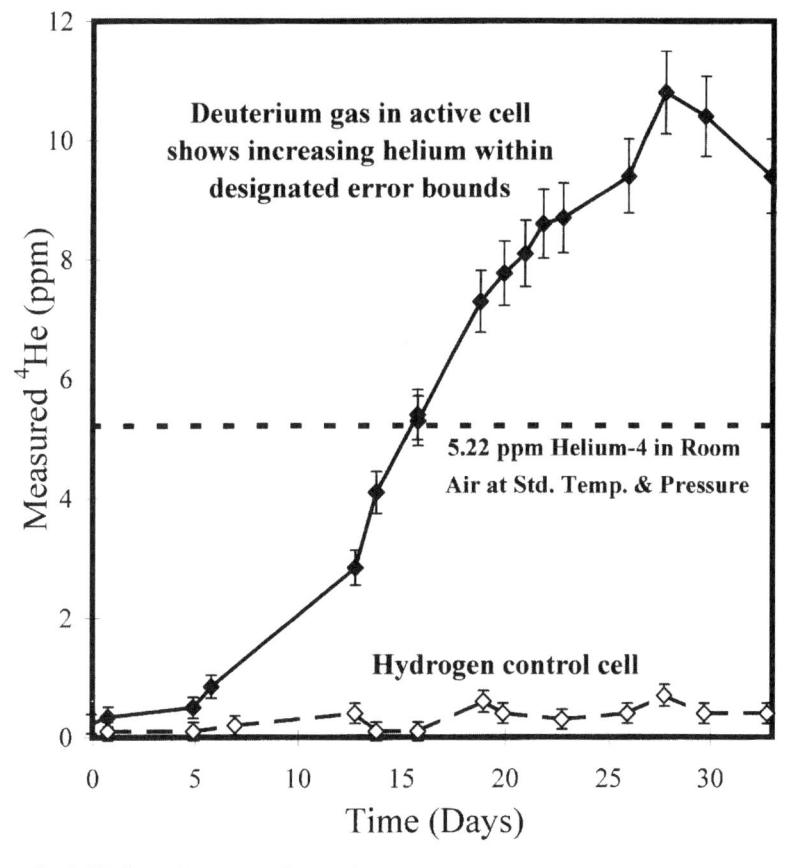

Figure 3-6. Helium Increase in Sealed Cells Containing Palladium on Carbon Catalyst (Les Case-Type Cell) Performed in Hydrogen and Deuterium Gas.[11]

In the next SRI International graph (Figure 3-7), the value of helium evolution shown in the prior graph is shown to correlate with the excess energy produced from the cell. Two different heat measurements (differential and gradient) are used and displayed. The helium values are plotted (noted as SC2), and the close temporal relationship between the generation of excess heat and the evolution of helium-4 is apparent.

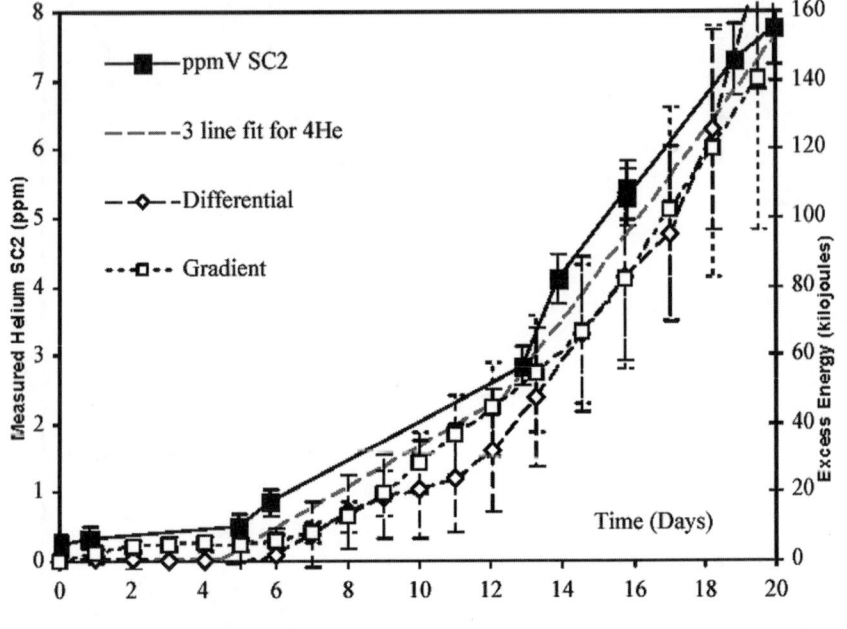

Figure 3-7. Correlation of Heat and Helium Production in Deuterium Gas
Cell

In hot fusion using deuterium, helium-4 is rarely observed; the probability is
on the order of one in 10 million compared to other fusion products, such as
tritium and neutrons. As well, in hot fusion, helium-4 is always accompanied
by a high-energy gamma ray.

Cold fusion scientists now know that, by contrast, in low-temperature fusion,
the dominant nuclear product is helium-4, along with the energy of 24
million electron volts. In a September 2003 e-mail, Del Giudice wrote, "The
appearance of helium, which was absent before the experiment, means
without any conceivable doubt that a nuclear reaction has taken place." [13]

Contrasting cold fusion with hot fusion, Nagel said, "The most remarkable
difference is that the helium-4 doesn't come out with the dangerous gamma
rays [radiation] as occur in hot fusion." This was considered a miracle that
many early cynics were unable to fathom because of their fixed beliefs and
entrenched theories. In cold fusion, Nagel explained, the excess energy "gets
coupled into the palladium lattice." Consequently, the reaction is influenced

200

by the solid structure of the palladium. "This," Nagel said, "is in contrast to what happens in the unbounded environment of free space in a plasma, where the excess energy is carried off by [deadly] gamma rays" or by other fast-moving particles.[14]

CHAPTER TWENTY-FOUR

Neutrons Found

In the early days of cold fusion research, many hot fusion scientists who investigated the validity of the cold fusion claims devoted concentrated effort to searching for neutrons. According to conventional nuclear theory, finding neutrons would verify the claims. Such emissions are considered unmistakable evidence of a nuclear reaction, as Rothwell noted:

> Hot fusion produces millions to hundreds of millions of times more neutrons per watt of heat than cold fusion, so the neutrons are easy to detect. You cannot miss them: The neutron flux from an unshielded 1-watt hot fusion reaction would kill the observer.

Finding no neutrons legitimized critics' skepticism toward the new discovery. But the situation was more complex. This was by no means an open-and-shut case.

Time would show, as Julian Schwinger, a Nobel laureate in physics, explained so eloquently, that the defense of cold fusion can be stated simply: "The circumstances of cold fusion are not those of hot fusion." In other words, generating fusion that looked and behaved differently was possible, if it were generated under different conditions than usual. In fact, the conditions and the outcome were inseparable.

This insight makes clear that the initial skepticism was misplaced. Neutrons are rarely produced in cold fusion. Alternatively, heat is the principal signature of the low temperature nuclear reaction, and helium-4, as just discussed, is its primary byproduct.

Heat is measured by calorimetry, a specialty relatively foreign to the nuclear physicists who investigated the claims. They neither understood nor trusted it. Therefore, in their minds, the chemists' excess heat evidence was inadmissible.

The electrochemists, on the other hand, were not only familiar with calorimetry but perfected the instrumentation for use with cold fusion research.

Interestingly, even though helium-4 and heat are the primary reaction products of cold fusion, some neutron emissions have been observed. Most cold fusion researchers have considered it not worth their while to look for neutrons, since they appear in such rare numbers. Furthermore, in the Fleischmann-Pons type of cold fusion experiments, neutrons are extremely hard to detect. As Rothwell noted, one must be an expert in calorimetry as well as nuclear physics to find them:

> It makes no sense to look for neutrons unless you are sure a reaction is under way, and the only way to be sure a reaction is under way is to measure excess heat. Scientists who insist on looking for neutrons while they ignore helium and excess heat resemble the drunk who drops his keys in the bushes but looks for them under the streetlight because it is too dark to see in the bushes.

One scientist who has been extremely successful in his study of excess heat as well as in finding neutron emissions is Tadahiko Mizuno of Hokkaido National University, Japan. Mizuno is an assistant professor of nuclear engineering and is credited with reporting the first extensive cold fusion neutron measurements in Japan.

Mizuno was no stranger to the electrolytic method used by Fleischmann and Pons; he had been doing similar experiments for 20 years. In the introduction to Mizuno's book, *Nuclear Transmutation: The Reality of Cold Fusion*, Rothwell wrote the following:

Within days of the 1989 announcement, Mizuno set to work on a "crude, preliminary" experiment. He built the cell in a single afternoon, which is, in itself, astonishing. His purpose was to detect neutrons, which he, along with everyone else in 1989, assumed would be the principal signature of the reaction. Months later, it became clear that heat is the principal signature and that neutrons appear [only] sporadically. The neutron flux is a million times smaller in proportion to the heat than it is with hot fusion. His colleague, Tadashi Akimoto, an expert in neutron detection, soon convinced him that the instrumentation must be improved and that the cell must be moved to a well-shielded location before meaningful results might be obtained. The underground laboratory housing the linear accelerator, close by on campus, was the ideal spot for the experiment, but it is hardly an ideal place for people. It is dark, dank, and unheated in winter, as Mizuno well knew from years of doing graduate research there. After weeks of operation, the experiment showed slight signs of generating 2.45 million electron volts of neutrons. Mizuno decided to get serious.

Here we learn what a real scientist is made of. While the rest of the world rushed to judgment, Mizuno buckled down and began a second "serious" experiment. The preparations took eight months. Mizuno and a graduate student worked long days building and testing the cell and preparing the anode, cathode, electrolyte, and controls. They planned to run at 100 degrees Celsius and 10 atmospheres of pressure, so they ran pressure tests at 150 degrees Celsius and 50 atmospheres, improving the seals and connections until they saw no significant pressure decline for days. Finally, they were ready to begin the first test run. The hysteria was long past. The press and the establishment had dismissed cold fusion. Real experiments by people like Mizuno were [just] getting under way. When these tests were finished and documented a year or two later, they constituted definitive proof of tritium, excess heat and transmutation. It is tempting to think that the tragedy of cold fusion boils down to ... a short attention span.

Mizuno has continued, year after year, to search for the answers in low energy nuclear experiments. In contrast to the cold fusion excess-heat experiments, low-level neutron emissions provide little or no apparent value to society as a possible energy source. However, the finding of low levels of neutrons is important because it establishes yet another telescope, if you will, to see the cold fusion phenomenon.

Physicist Steven Jones of Brigham Young University in Utah also has seen increasingly successful experiments that demonstrate neutron emissions. At the 10th International Conference on Cold Fusion, in Cambridge, Massachusetts, in 2003, he reported a yield of 57 neutrons (fusion reactions) counted per hour in a recent experiment.[1]

Jones is the creator of the term "cold fusion," coined several years before the 1989 Fleischmann-Pons announcement; however, he had used it to describe a significantly different phenomenon. Jones' experiments have nothing to do with excess heat, the most important aspect of the Fleischmann-Pons work.

Unfortunately, most of the press confused the two, and as history would have it, the name "cold fusion" is how everyone knows the Fleischmann-Pons discovery.

While Jones' experiments do not generate excess heat or helium-4, they are, indeed, verifiable low energy nuclear reactions, though a flux of 57 neutrons per hour is a markedly smaller nuclear reaction, by 11 orders of magnitude, than with the Fleischmann-Pons excess heat effect.[2]

Nuclear Evidence: Setting the Record Straight

Ten years ago, Professor John Huizenga, who led the 1989 Department of Energy cold fusion panel, asserted, "Room-temperature nuclear fusion without commensurate amounts of fusion products is a delusion and qualifies as pathological science." [3] If any truth ever existed to Huizenga's cynical comment, none remains now. The landmark evidence showing helium-4 and excess heat correlation has rendered such assessments erroneous.

The premature judgments by Huizenga and other science authorities with vested interests in conventional fusion research derailed the scientific process and distracted the public interest from an honest dialogue.

In Richard Garwin's Dec. 23, 1993, report to the Pentagon, he stated, "Of course, all of us would be fascinated and would feel great admiration if it were possible reliably to produce excess heat. ... The same would be true of a new way of producing nuclear particles under such circumstances." On Sept. 3, 2004, in a telephone call, Garwin expressed reluctance to take cold fusion seriously because, among other reasons, it showed poor reproducibility. He defined good reproducibility as results that are positive "more often than not." Now that these achievements have come to pass, the scientific establishment should show the cold fusion researchers, who have persisted in the face of daunting challenges and unfair cynicism, great admiration.

David Nagel decided to set the record straight. In his public address at the 10th International Conference on Cold Fusion, he concluded:

> There are many, many cold fusion experiments in which [the nuclear evidence] is nowhere near marginal, ... with strong, robust signal-to-noise ratios and many standard deviations for the data above the background noise. If the experiments which were performed by capable and careful workers ... and good calibrated equipment do hold up - and I'll bet my retirement they do, then ... it's not chemistry! ... You can burn the whole experiment, and you can't get that [amount of energy] out. You cannot make helium or tritium by chemistry. ... We are talking about a *nuclear effect* at low energies, ordinary temperatures.[4]

207

CHAPTER TWENTY-FIVE

The Race for a Nobel Prize-Winning Theory

Many early critics prematurely dismissed cold fusion research because of the lack of a proven theory. Beaudette explained the error of such criticism:

> [Critics] failed to realize that science, at the beginning, does not expect or require understanding. That would become the *continuing* purpose of scientific study. In 1903, Pierre Curie did not understand the self-heating of radium, ... and in 1911, Dr. H.K. Onnes did not understand what enabled superconductivity. Nevertheless, both won Nobel prizes."[1]

McKubre recalled his own introduction to the paradigm-breaking cold fusion phenomenon:

> Having seen the effect with my own eyes, the claims from a few that this is impossible, inconsistent with all known laws of nuclear physics, these suggestions are in fact irrelevant. There is, in fact, no theoretical objection to cold fusion; it's just unlikely, given our experience with hot fusion.[2]

As of the 10th International Conference on Cold Fusion, several theories show how the Fleischmann-Pons cold fusion effect demonstrates excess heat, without lethal radiation. The theories also explain how nuclear fusion is possible at low temperatures. Both anomalies stand in complete contradiction to 70 years of research and accepted theory which apply to *hot* fusion but not to *cold* fusion.

To date, however, none of the cold fusion theories is complete. "While major experimental progress has been made," Nagel told the conference audience, complete "understanding still eludes us." He said, "In terms of asking theory to do what it normally does - explain the past and predict the future - we're not quite there yet." [3]

At least seven scientists, all physicists, have entered the race to explain cold fusion. The eventual winner must be able to explain how, at room temperature, atomic nuclei can overcome what is known as the "coulomb barrier," a powerful, repulsive electromagnetic force which prevents atomic nuclei from joining together easily. In addition, the theory will have to explain how the energy and momentum from the fusion reaction are conserved by being transferred to the palladium lattice as a whole, rather than to a gamma ray or other fast-moving particle, as is normally the case with hot fusion. [4]

While quite a few cold fusion theories have been proposed, little consensus exists among the theoreticians. Several, such as Hagelstein of MIT, former Naval Research Laboratory physicist Talbot Chubb, and his uncle, theoretical physicist Scott Chubb of Research Systems Inc., have offered models which, they say, explain the cold fusion observations almost completely as well as predict results. The approaches are surprisingly diverse in nature.

Hagelstein, a professor of electrical engineering and computer science at MIT, is credited with designing the X-ray laser for President Reagan's Star Wars program. Hagelstein reportedly has developed one of the more complete theories. He said the following in a January 2004 e-mail:

> I examined more than 100 models and variants before arriving at the model currently under investigation. ... The new models can be understood perhaps simply. Instead of formulating nuclear reactions in a vacuum, as is done in nuclear physics textbooks, the proposal is that one needs to begin with a formulation that includes the [metal] lattice at the outset. [5]

Hagelstein's theory explains that the nuclear energy is transferred to the palladium lattice in the form of heat, through phonons, to accomplish this miraculous feat.

Ten years ago, Dr. Edward Teller, known as one of the great physicists of our time and as the father of the hydrogen bomb, requested that McKubre provide him with an update on the status of cold fusion. Teller was not ready to endorse cold fusion by the end of McKubre's presentation. However, he reportedly told McKubre that, if a cold fusion effect did exist, he "could encompass an explanation of it with a very small change in the laws of physics." [6]

University of Tennessee Professor J. Reece Roth, an esteemed, 46-year expert in fusion energy, 10-time patent awardee, and author of a college textbook titled *Introduction to Fusion Energy*, made a similar comment. In a telephone conversation in November 2003, he said that developments in cold fusion theory within the past five years have begun to expand the scope of known physics in a way that can better explain both cold *and* hot fusion.

Roth spoke about the work of nuclear physicist Dr. Xing Zhong Li, which was published in *Physical Review C* in 2000. Li is a professor at Tsinghua University, which is regarded as the MIT of China. In Li's paper, titled "Sub-Barrier Fusion and Selective Resonant Tunneling," he, like Hagelstein, returned to the origins of fusion calculations which were developed in the 1930s and 1940s. [7]

Fusion calculations use the term "cross section," which represents the probability that two particles may fuse, given a specific material, over a range of temperatures.

Li found that the original cross sections were based on experimental data taken at various labs because they were initially of interest for H-bombs. Roth noted the following:

> The measured cross sections were phenomenologically fit to a formula that was basically pulled out of thin air, rather than a formula derived from first principles, which would allow one to calculate what the cross sections should be as a function of, for example, energy. ... Until Li's theory came along, no one could understand how and why the reported observations could occur on the basis of known physics. Li has expanded the scope of known physics in a way that can explain how you could have cold fusion.

Having done that then, the reasons why it can't work that applied prior to his theory just simply are irrelevant.

In other words, Li found an improper initial assumption with the original fusion formulas. Correcting this assumption, Roth said, "greatly simplified the mathematics and the nature of the cross-section calculations of the original fusion reactions." Li explained to Roth that some of his calculations were derived from quantum mechanics, where two [deuterium nuclei] within the lattice are treated as colliding waves. Furthermore, Roth stated:

> I told Professor Li and my students when he was here last that, if he's correct, I'll have to throw away about 14 of the 16 chapters in my book *Introduction to Fusion Energy* because it will no longer be relevant to the kinds of fusion that could result from this cold fusion process.[8]

Li made a historic "first" in the field of fusion science. As an update to his 2000 paper, he published a follow-up paper in 2002 titled "Nuclear Physics for Nuclear Fusion" in the journal *Fusion Science and Technology* which introduced an astounding finding.[9]

In this paper, he corrected a mistake in the nuclear cross-section data published by the U.S. National Nuclear Data Center at Brookhaven Laboratory. Li wrote, "This is the first time a correction has been made to *hot fusion data* based on *cold fusion theory*." Understandably, he reported that the editor-in-chief was extremely hesitant to publish the result, but after numerous communications with the National Data Center and the journal, they eventually concurred with his findings.[10]

Li concluded his paper with the simple statement which heralds the possible end to polluting and dangerous energy sources:

> In conclusion, the nuclear physics for sub-barrier [cold] fusion provides a new approach toward nuclear fusion energy with no strong nuclear radiation.[11]

CHAPTER TWENTY-SIX

Nuclear Energy from Normal Water

Quite a few scientists in the cold fusion field are striving to understand an even more unusual set of observations than the excess heat-generating palladium-deuterium reaction. In the early 1990s, scientists found evidence of nuclear reactions occurring in normal water. These experiments are often referred to as "light water" low energy nuclear reactions. However, some scientists consider the term "light water" to be technically imprecise, because true "light" water is devoid of deuterium, whereas normal water has trace amounts of deuterium, one for every 6,000 hydrogen atoms.[1]

In the experiments with light water, the process of fusion cannot readily explain the effect, because deuterium atoms are present only in trace amounts. Yet some remarkable, as-yet-unexplained reactions are occurring. The light water experiments yield some excess heat, though not as much as the heavy water experiments. However, nuclear transmutations of heavy elements, with dozens of protons in their nucleus, having a much greater mass than mere tritium or helium, have been observed. While such observations have long been accepted in the field of high-energy physics, to make such claims using chemistry smacks of medieval alchemy and draws forth no small protests from orthodox science.

Early in the history of cold fusion research, a chemist formerly with Dow Chemical Co., Dr. James Patterson, applied a unique electrolytic method that he had used for other purposes in prior years. Patterson is credited with 16 U.S. patents in the area. Jean Paul Biberian, formerly with the French Atomic Energy Commission and chairman of the 11th International Conference on Cold Fusion, offered a description of Patterson's light water research:

[Patterson] uses small plastic beads about one millimeter in diameter, coated with nickel, palladium and again with nickel, each layer about one micron - very thin layers. Cold fusion seems to be a surface effect phenomenon. It doesn't seem to be an effect from the bulk of the palladium. It's coming from the surface. So by using this thin film technique with small beads, you have a lot of surface but very little bulk. It has something to do with the loading of deuterium in the crystal lattice. If you start the [experiment] with thin films, you load them much faster. And that's the big surprise. You start producing excess heat almost right away. By the time we do the measurements, there's already excess heat [appearing].[2]

Biberian's entrance into cold fusion research is an interesting story. Many years ago, he had won a lawsuit against the French Atomic Energy Commission for infringement on his patent on field emission flat panel display technology. At the time, he knew that an electrochemist named Georges Lonchampt was working for the commission performing cold fusion research.

Biberian's interest in cold fusion was just developing, though he had no funding of his own to perform the research. As a settlement for the lawsuit, he negotiated a hefty award with the director of the commission and, to top it off, agreed to a unique arrangement:

Because I wanted more than the limit, they offered me a good amount of money plus a three-year contract to work for them on cold fusion in Grenoble.[3]

With the hard feelings aside, and cash in pocket, he gladly accepted the opportunity to receive funding for his passion, cold fusion research.

The use of other elements besides palladium, as Patterson's research demonstrates, is an exciting extension of the field. Storms has seen several advantages:

It's made it obvious that there is a wide spectrum of chemical environments in which these nuclear reactions can occur. Some of these environments are much easier to produce than others. In particular, it's easier to produce in the nickel system than in the palladium system. But it depends on how you go about doing it, too. The electrolytic technique is very difficult, whereas the ultrasonic loading technique is much easier. So it depends on how you put the hydrogen or deuterium into the metal, and it depends on what the metal is.[4]

Another exciting aspect of light water research was noted by Miley in a paper presented at the 10th International Conference on Cold Fusion. To date, Miley said, light water experiments have generated a low level of excess power because of the small amount of metal in the films. However, he continued, "the specific power density [that is, the capacity of a particular quantity of palladium to generate power relative to its own mass] is 10 to 100 times that of the typical solid-electrode [heavy water] experiments. Thus, a scale-up in power could be obtained using multiple electrodes."

In the paper, Miley stated, "The ultimate objective is to achieve 100-watt to 20-kilowatt units for distributed power network applications [that is, small power units for homes and businesses]." [5] This design is of particular interest because of its potential to be manufactured by existing microelectronic production facilities.[6] Still, researchers need to gain control over a multitude of variables before resolving the critical commercial issues of longevity and controllability pertaining to such power sources.

CHAPTER TWENTY-SEVEN

Nuclear Transmutations Through Chemistry

According to a 2003 survey performed by Miley, nuclear transmutations have been observed in 15 separate laboratories worldwide (See Appendix B) in both H_2O (light) and D_2O (heavy) water experiments: [1]

In one of the most profound and well-documented sets of research experiments in the area of low temperature nuclear transmutation, researchers at Japan's Mitsubishi Heavy Industries note one experimental run which generated up to 3.2 watts of excess power and, in the process, transmuted one metal into another.

The creative genius for this work comes from Yasuhiro Iwamura. In a highly controlled environment, the Mitsubishi team, using deuterium gas rather than heavy water, created titanium atoms from a multi-layer cathode of palladium and calcium oxide. In his 1998 paper, Iwamura explained:

> Titanium atoms, which cannot be explained by contamination, were detected on the surface where deuterium atoms passed through on palladium cathodes after electrolysis. ... Excess heat generation and X-ray emissions were observed for all the cases we tried by the multi-layer cathodes.

Their configuration allowed them to measure the growing elements – in situ as the experiment was running. Each of their five runs was successful. They also detected measurable traces of other heavy elements, including iron and copper.[2]

Nuclear transmutation, the creation of one element from another, is profound for two reasons. First, it has been a long-sought-after mystery since the time of the medieval alchemists, whom history regards as charlatans for their attempts to convert lead into gold. Second, while the creation of a few titanium atoms and some excess heat by the use of $10 million worth of apparatus is certainly not a cost-effective method to make new elements, that such reactions can occur outside of high-energy physics laboratories, at low temperatures, is a profound proof-of-concept.

In 2002, further developments of the Mitsubishi work were published in the *Japanese Journal of Applied Physics*. The paper described the continuation of their work using thin films of palladium and calcium oxide. Iwamura reported two sets of transmutations that resulted from applying other elements to the palladium film. In the first set, Iwamura said, "when cesium was added on the surface of a palladium complex, praseodymium emerged on the surface while cesium decreased." [3] Iwamura explained his objectives for this experiment:

> I had previously observed transmutation reactions of carbon and lithium, but their products were silicon, sulfur and aluminum, all common elements. It was very difficult to prove that these common elements were nuclear products. I chose cesium because I thought it might be transmuted into a rare earth element, and fortunately, I obtained praseodymium.[4]

In his second experiment, strontium was placed on the surface of the thin film of palladium, and molybdenum emerged while the strontium decreased. Experiments that ran without the specific palladium and calcium oxide complex did not show positive results, nor did experiments which ran with hydrogen gas instead of deuterium gas. In the control for the praseodymium experiment, Iwamura said he found "that cesium did not change and praseodymium never appeared." He said "that deuterium is a necessary factor for observing the anomalous behavior of cesium and praseodymium."

Confirmation came in August 2003, when scientists at Osaka University, Japan, announced at the 10th International Conference on Cold Fusion that they had replicated the Mitsubishi work. The lead scientist on the Osaka team was Taichi Higashiyama. The work was performed within the Department of Nuclear Engineering of the Graduate School of Engineering. The chair of the nuclear instrumentation group, Professor Akito Takahashi, described the replication:

> We replicated the Mitsubishi experiment three times and each time transmuted praseodymium from cesium. Our reproducibility on this experiment is 100 percent so far.[5]

Takahashi noted that external verification of the results was performed by a sophisticated analysis at the Japan Atomic Energy Research Institute, which also confirmed this historic evidence of a low energy nuclear reaction.

CHAPTER TWENTY-EIGHT

Technical Summary of Cold Fusion

This chapter is for the more technical reader. It presents a branching diagram of cold fusion reaction paths that summarizes the variety of known reaction products and their respective environments. It also provides a technical explanation of the cold fusion effect.

The branching diagram in Figure 3-8 is based on an earlier version by James Corey and should be considered a work-in-progress, as greater understanding of the field evolves. Two advisory notes are appropriate.

First, not all methods and variations of cold fusion experiments are depicted. Readers may find further information in Storms' paper, "Cold Fusion: An Objective Assessment," on the Internet at www.edstorms.com.

Second, several cold fusion researchers have expressed strong differences of opinion as to both the magnitude of excess heat and the veracity of transmutations in normal water experiments. The opinions vary, as one might expect, based on individuals' respective area of expertise and hands-on experience.

The primary results of the heavy water and deuterium gas experiments are understood to be excess heat, helium-4 and, occasionally, small amounts of tritium. Normal water experiments show excess heat and various nuclear transmutations, with mass numbers spanning the periodic table. Deuterium gas experiments have been shown to yield primarily transmutations of heavy elements along with some tritium and helium.

Tritium and helium-3 are seen only on rare occasions, and the presence of helium-3 may be a result from evolved tritium, which rapidly decays to helium-3.

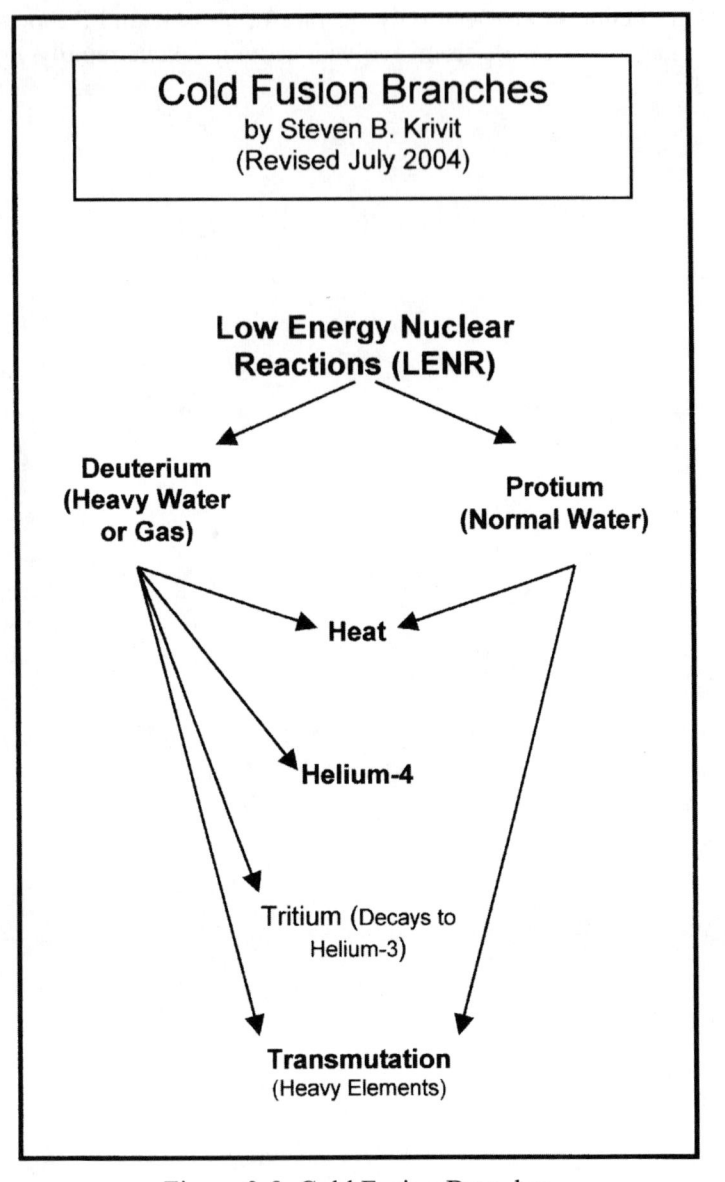

Figure 3-8. Cold Fusion Branches

The Cold Fusion Effect: A Technical Explanation

The following explanation repeats some portions of earlier text in this book. This explanation, however, goes into greater technical depth and includes all the pertinent aspects. As with the diagram above, this explanation should be considered a work-in-progress and will evolve over time:

> In a nuclear fusion process, two atomic nuclei usually combine to make a new larger nucleus and often a lighter particle (such as a proton or neutron) and energy.
>
> In accordance with Einstein's equation, $E=mc^2$, the energy arises from a loss of mass. In fusion, the mass of the new nucleus together with the lighter particle (if present) is slightly less than the mass of the two initial nuclei.
>
> Two nuclei strongly repel each other, and they must be forced together somehow before fusion will occur. In conventional thermonuclear, or hot fusion, as in the sun, extremely high temperature (10 million degrees) supplies the necessary force.
>
> Many methods of deuterium-deuterium cold fusion experiments exist, in both liquid and gas forms. The basic cold fusion experiment is performed in a relatively simple electrolysis apparatus at or near room temperature. Scientists immerse two pieces of metal, a palladium cathode (negatively charged) and a platinum anode (positively charged), in a beaker containing a conductive solution of D_2O (heavy water), containing LiOD (lithium deuteroxide). An electrical current is passed through the solution between the two metal conductors. Deuterium is released from the heavy water at the cathode, where it either tries to escape as a gas or enters the crystalline atomic structure of the palladium (lattice). This method allows a very high concentration of deuterium to be achieved in the palladium without having to apply very high gas pressure.

If precise parameters and requirements are met, the reaction generates excess heat and ordinary helium. Excess heat means that more energy exits the experiment than entered it.

Conventional nuclear fusion of deuterium makes light helium (helium-3), tritium, protons and neutrons. Ordinary helium (helium-4) also is produced in conventional nuclear fusion, but only on rare occasions. When helium-4 is produced in hot fusion, not only is energy released in a way that is consistent with the change in mass (associated with Einstein's $E=mc^2$ equation), but the reaction also is known to cause subtle effects involving the behavior of the deuterium nuclei, far away from the location where the ordinary helium is produced. Briefly and simply stated, these effects are observed as gamma radiation and are deadly to humans.

How two deuterium nuclei can approach close enough to fuse at room temperature is not clear, even in palladium. However, the amounts of excess heat in cold fusion are consistent with the change in energy that results when heavy hydrogen is converted into helium-4. Most scientists who have been studying the subject believe that this particular effect is related to subtle differences between the fusion processes, associated with the helium-4 reaction. No high-energy gamma radiation is seen in cold fusion.

Unfortunately, because it was initially assumed that cold fusion is a "colder" form of conventional nuclear fusion, most scientists assumed that light helium or tritium had to be produced. For this reason, they ignored the possibility that ordinary helium might be involved and concluded that the excess-heat cold fusion phenomenon either did not involve nuclear fusion or, alternatively, could be the result of some other, as-yet-unknown nuclear process.

With time, scientists researching cold fusion have learned that the excess-heat effect is only one of many nuclear phenomena that can take place when deuterium atoms are forced into a solid. For this reason, the term "low energy nuclear reaction" is a more technically accurate descriptor than "cold fusion."

Because of the confusion that resulted from the assumption that cold fusion is a "colder" version of nuclear fusion, it is apparent not only that the name is inappropriate but also that the use of this name has adversely affected the field.

For better or for worse, the name has remained, and the term "cold fusion effect," which also has been used, serves as a shortcut for the unexplained reaction observed in these experiments.

Part Four

REFLECTION AND ANTICIPATION

CHAPTER TWENTY-NINE

Threats to Academic Freedom

Researchers' freedom to study what interests them and what, in their view, may be of potential value to society, is essential for the progress of humanity. If departments of science limit research to the realm of what is known and accepted, no further scientific breakthroughs can occur.

Philip W. Anderson, in his article titled "Why Do They Leave Physics?" described a pervasive mindset that fosters conformity and stifles innovation:

> The members of our profession, particularly those who have the responsibility for hiring and for funding research, are infected with "Horganism," the belief that the end of science (or at least of our science) is at hand and that all that is left to do is to grub away at Kuhnian "normal science" following the accepted paradigms. They believe that there are no more scientific revolutions possible and that we are now in pursuit of nothing but the next decimal place.

Anderson also conveyed the thoughts of one of his former students, who elected to discontinue his career in academia for a job that not only paid him handsomely but also offered him essential non-monetary rewards:

> There are several reasons for wanting to leave academia, not the least being the desire for a ... work environment which ... rewards those who take appropriate risks. ... The problems I have been attracted to ... are motivated by real-world data where there is no ... existing theoretical model. Involvement in such projects ... requires a desire for new challenges, an appetite for risk, and the ability to be innovative yet humble in the face of ... data.[1]

Cold fusion has been one such category of research that has confronted the rigid expectations of academia. For sure, cold fusion has been kept alive by a hearty and dedicated breed of researchers. Virtually no research funding and, for the most part, no recognition have come to those who dare explore this forbidden field.

The disincentives are immense, Michael McKubre said in an Aug. 8, 2003, interview. "There is strong inertia in support of the status quo and harsh punishment meted out to those who seek to disrupt it," McKubre said. Those in government research have risked political disfavor; those in academia have risked ostracism and demotion.[2]

Many, if not all, who have participated in this new scientific revolution first-hand have made tremendous sacrifices. Most people know that Martin Fleischmann and Stanley Pons were never able return to academic study. Others have learned to be cautious when challenging the status quo. Peter Hagelstein came very close to losing his position in academia because of his interests in cold fusion, as he wrote in a Dec. 15, 1993, letter to John Bockris:

> Early on, a number of my colleagues encouraged me to consider what might be happening, in case Pons and Fleischmann were right, that a heat effect existed. I first considered a scenario in which fusion could occur as a coherent process. Due to the local politics at MIT, even the mere consideration of such a scenario attracted media attention and came very close to costing me my job.

A prominent cold fusion theoretician working at Purdue University declined to go on record for this book because of the fear that he, too, would suffer undue persecution if his interests in cold fusion were known. Many others have been reticent and have contributed to this book only reluctantly.

Certainly, the cold fusion pioneer who most challenged the limits of academic freedom, next to Fleischmann and Pons, was Bockris. His explorations into previously condemned subject matter outraged his fellow university professors. Fortunately, Bockris was undaunted by their perceptions of him as unscientific, unethical or heretical.

Centuries after alchemy had been established as the quintessential fraudulent science, and years before the current body of evidence for nuclear transmutations through low energy nuclear reactions had accumulated, Bockris dared to pursue the idea of transmuting mercury and lead into gold. The idea was proposed by an outside experimenter named Joe Champion, whom Bockris accepted into his laboratory. Champion brought with him funding from an associate named William Telander. Bockris was thrilled about the possibility of a real scientific basis for transmuting base elements into precious metals.

Melvin Miles reported that Champion and Telander also contacted him to attempt the gold-making scheme:

> They wanted to come to China Lake as well as some other laboratories; they were really quite persuasive. However, Bob Nowak, the funding officer at the Navy's Office of Naval Research, decided that we should not get involved. We didn't know if we could trust them.[3]

Bockris would later learn what others suspected, that the two had unscientific motives; however, at the time, he resisted what might have been his better judgment and allowed himself to get involved with these two characters.

Much has been written of these events, and although most accounts are factual, a subtle but important distinction has been either omitted or misrepresented in nearly all reports. Bockris was unmistakably thrilled with the prospect of transmuting base elements into precious metals. However, his motives were scientific, not commercial, as he explained:

> Telander's great aim was to make cheap gold, but we never got more than the tiniest bits of gold; on perhaps two or three occasions, we saw tiny specks. But Telander, who wasn't of course a scientist, had thought that once we had detected tiny amounts of gold, we could make huge amounts! I did explain to him very gently that, if he was able to sell it very cheaply, then the prices of gold would fall, and he wouldn't be able to make much money, anyway.[4]

Certainly, if transmuting base to precious metals could succeed, the value to society is dubious. However, if the general nature of Bockris' heavy-element transmutation research turns out to demonstrate the foundation of technology that might transmute toxic radioactive waste into harmless materials, this is another matter and is of immense value to society.

What occurred shortly thereafter was nearly identical to the account that Galileo wrote, as quoted earlier in this book:

> The novelty of these things, as well as some consequences which followed from them in contradiction to the physical notions commonly held among academic philosophers, stirred up against me no small number of professors.

Bockris described the reaction from his peers at Texas A&M University:

> In December 1993, [Frank Albert Cotton], a professor of inorganic chemistry organized the writing of a petition to have the distinguished professors ask that my distinguished professorship be removed from me "for this cold fusion caper." Most signed the petition, none asking if there were refereed publications (there were six at the time).[5]

The document written and circulated by Cotton was titled "A REQUEST." It seemed hastily written, as shown by the grammatical and logical errors:

> Professor J. O'M. Bockris' activities since 1989 (the inception of the "cold fusion" embroglio), and particularly recent allegations that he lent his name and that of our university to a fraudulent scheme to promote a bogus engineering enterprise, has brought this university into disrepute. Note that on page 6 of the "Policies and Procedures Regarding Distinguished Professor Appointments" (September, 1993) it is stated that "The Distinguished Professors ... bring honor and recognition to the University." ... Instead, we believe that Bockris' recent activities has made the terms "Texas A&M" and "Aggie" objects of derisive laughter throughout the world among scientists and engineers, not to mention a large segment of the lay public. The "Alchemy" caper is, everywhere, a sure trigger for sniggering at our university. And so it should be. For a trained scientist to claim, or support anyone else's claim, to have transmuted elements is difficult for us to believe and is no more acceptable than to claim to have invented a gravity shield, revived the dead, or to be

mining green cheese on the moon. We believe it is sheer nonsense, and, in our opinion, could not have been done innocently by one with a lifetime of experience in one of the physical sciences.

In view of the above considerations, we the undersigned Distinguished Professors of Texas A&M University hereby request the Provost to take steps to revoke the title of Distinguished Professor now carried by John O'M. Bockris. We do this because of our belief that Dr. Bockris' alleged disregard of the accepted standards of scholarly and professional behavior has brought great embarrassment upon this university and his colleagues. In our opinion he no longer merits the title of Distinguished Professor.

[Signatures]

Dr. Perry L. Adkisson, Entomology, Dr. Richard Arnowitt, Physics, Sir Derek Barton, Chemistry, Dr. Charles K. Chui, Mathematics, Dr. F. Albert Cotton, Chemistry, Dr. Michael J. Duff, Physics, Dr. John Fackler, Chemistry, Dr. Timothy Hall, Biology, Dr. Hamlin Hill, English, Dr. Charles F. Kettleborough, Mechanical Engineering, Dr. Arthur E. Martell, Chemistry, Dr. Dimitri Nanopoulos, Physics, Dr. Gerald North, Meteorology and Oceanography, Dr. Worth Nowlin, Oceanography, Dr. Emanuel Parzen, Statistics, Dr. Herbert Richardson, Engineering, Dr. Stephen Safe, Veterinary Physiology, Dr. Thomas R. Saving, Economics, Dr. Donald T. Sawyer, Chemistry, Dr. A Ian Scott, Chemistry, Dr. Max Summers, Entomology, Dr. Frank E. Vandiver, History

The context makes clear the immense pressure to conform. The request was accompanied by a document titled "Notes on the Signing of the Request" (by F.A. Cotton). The document explains the stated reasons for those who abstained from signing for all but one distinguished professor. The organizers of this effort clearly intended to leave no stone unturned. The only non-signer whose reason for abstention was not written is noted in the document as follows: "Professor X has a compelling personal reason, which must remain confidential, for being unable to sign." The professor's name was withheld for reasons that shortly will become apparent, as will his reasons for refusing to sign.

On Jan. 17, 1994, the brother of Professor X wrote the following to administrators at Texas A&M University:

Dear Dr. Kraemer,

My brother, Professor X, is a "Distinguished Professor" of [department withheld] at Texas A&M University (and, I have heard, the only such who declined to sign a petition demanding the resignation of Distinguished Professor John Bockris for allegedly damaging the prestige of Texas A&M University). However, my brother had been abroad for several months when the furor erupted, and our 89-year old mother, who also lives in College Station and who has heard me express admiration for Dr. Bockris, mailed me numerous and lengthy inflammatory articles from your local press, so that I was aware of this brouhaha before my brother returned to the United States. I was so appalled at the articles in your local press that I told my mother that I was going to write a letter to the editor attempting to set the record straight. However, she begged me not to do it, on the grounds that "it might damage Professor X's reputation to be associated with this furor." But now that the slanderous article has appeared ... (and my brother - God bless him! - has returned to the United States and manfully declined to join in the lynch mob), I am going to submit an "op ed" piece about this matter ... and advise them to set their investigative reporters to start digging into the real truth of the matter.

This attempt to "get" Bockris has nothing to do with "alchemy" and everything to do with Dr. Bockris' principled and well-informed dissent from the dogma of the "scientific establishment" to the effect that cold fusion is "impossible," an incompetent dogma which in a few years will be recognized by the entire world as not only misguided scientifically but misguided for reprehensible motives: to maintain the status quo in the scientific pecking order, with physicists as the proud keepers of fundamental knowledge and high energy physicists ... as the high priests of physics.

Professor X's brother reported that, when Professor X was asked to sign the petition letter, he was "hauled in front of [a professor] and a Dean ... yelled and screamed at ... in an attempt to get [him] to sign the anti-Bockris petition.

234

... [A professor] had yelled at [him], 'I am the second most-cited chemist in the world!!!'" in outrage at Professor X's refusal to sign.

Professor X was contacted for further details on this story; however, he was extremely fearful of his story appearing in print. In a Sept. 3, 2004, e-mail, he wrote, "It had better not [appear in print] or I will take it to court" and then denied the story that his brother told. Professor X then offered a contradictory and confusing version of the story.

Highly emotional e-mails from both Professor X and his brother explained that further public association with the matter would bring severe emotional stress to each of them, and they demanded anonymity.

The request to have Bockris demoted contained major errors, as Gene Mallove immediately noticed. The greatest flaw was the misconception that transmuted elements could not occur in known science:

> Are we to understand that the petitioners do not acknowledge the viability of transmuting elements in nuclear particle accelerators, in fission reactions, and in radioactive decay? Clearly, this cannot be, for they each must have a modicum of scientific training, whatever their fields. They apparently intended to attack the idea of *low-energy* transmutation of elements, but they were not careful in so qualifying their petition. Hence, they have literally made fools of themselves by signing that document. This is not a small point! It indicates the haste with which these · gentlemen assembled themselves into a mob to attack Professor Bockris.[6]

Peter Hagelstein sympathized with Bockris in view of the fact that even the transmutation of deuterium to helium in cold fusion could be considered alchemy:

> I assume that, by the time you receive this letter, your colleagues will have stoked the kindling at the base of a very large stake with your name on it and will ultimately succeed in this way in cleansing your soul of the scientific errors that in their view you have made. *And after you, others.*

> But after some reflection, what has been discussed in the cold fusion [field] could be classified under one of the definitions of alchemy in the American College Dictionary. Altering nuclei through essentially chemical means is the heart of alchemy, losing the immediate focus on the production of gold.

> Good luck in the trials ahead that are facing you. Judging by historical precedent, I suspect that you will in fact get burned at the stake, in spite of my input or input from anybody else.[7]

Another letter of support for Bockris came from Janos H. Fendler, a distinguished professor of chemistry with Syracuse University (New York). Fendler's Jan. 16, 1993, letter spoke directly to the point of academic freedom:

> Let me, at the onset, state that I am not qualified to make a valued scientific judgment on the merit of Professor Bockris' research. This, however, is not the issue. The issue is academic freedom to pursue research and express opinion, regardless of the controversy it may create. The issue is the recognition and respect of an eminent, world-class scientist. The issue is sanity and human dignity. Equally important, the issue is Texas A&M University's ability to handle its inquiry thoroughly and fairly.

> The history of science is full of controversies. Originality and creativity have always met with skepticism. Sometimes, this skepticism becomes nasty and degenerates into a personal vendetta. Judging by some press reports, John Bockris has become, in fact, the victim of a well-orchestrated malicious campaign and has been found guilty of misconduct without a proper hearing. The purpose of academic freedom and tenure is to permit the pursuit of scientific research, even against overwhelming antagonism. This is being done in most universities and is fostered in great ones.

The effects of the inquiry extended to Bockris' wife and their personal life, as well. During the course of the inquiry, Bockris reported that he once found feces in his mailbox at school. His wife, Lillian Bockris, reported that, while she was shopping in the town, people she knew would turn their heads and

236

would not acknowledge her. She and many others in the cold fusion community appealed to the university administration:

> Throughout the public lynching and the harassment my husband now has to suffer, throughout his defamation and denunciation made to the media by "professors who wish to remain anonymous" as well as letters and rumors to the media by Drs. Kemp, Fackler, Cotton, Duff and Wakefield, my husband has kept silent.

> The public and students are well aware that Professor Bockris has remained a gentleman and a scholar, much in contrast to the unprofessional public belligerence and ridicule displayed by the administration and some of the faculty members. ... It has been a merciless harassment, culminating in Dr. Cotton's ... "Request."[8]

Bockris said that his wife endured far more pain and suffering than any professor's wife should ever have to experience:

> My wife was a victim of the Nazi occupation of Austria and a refugee who reached America in a British liner convoyed by warships. She has told me that, during the years she lived in Vienna under the Nazis, she never felt so rejected and threatened as in College Station, Texas, 1992-95.[9]

Inevitably, and to the credit of at least some of the administration at Texas A&M, a Jan. 31, 1994, letter by Duane C. Kraemer, John C. Slattery, John J. McDermott and John C. Calhoun, Jr. advised Vice President Robert A. Kennedy that "it is the unanimous decision of this committee that a Committee of Investigation is not warranted." The Committee of Inquiry, as the four were called, "found there to be no evidence to sustain the charges." The letter said, "Consequently, the Committee holds Professor Bockris to be exonerated of these charges."

In a 2004 interview with Bockris, the authors of this book asked whether he regretted his choice of subject matter or whether he ever had any concerns about what others would think of him. Bockris responded:

> No, I didn't feel either embarrassed or afraid. I was quite sure of the results I published. This all went through a refereeing process in the

journal's editorial office, and after that, why should I be afraid? Certainly, I was given a drubbing by the scientists at Texas A&M and doubtless by others, but I knew that I had made discoveries, and the fate of those who changed the course of science is often preceded by reproaches, so I decided to grin and bear it.

Mike Epstein summed up the entire imbroglio succinctly in a 1994 paper titled "Academic Freedom or Scientific Misconduct?":

> I would remind those who seek [Bockris'] ouster or demotion that their actions threaten the core of academic freedom. Extraordinary claims require extraordinary proof, but no one should be punished for attempting to provide that proof.[10]

CHAPTER THIRTY

National Security

Threats to Economic Stability

Over a decade ago, two messengers summoned the attention of their respective countries' leaders, in the United States and in the Republic of Germany, to request that they hasten their support for cold fusion research. They expressed concern for their countries' economic welfare relative to their low prioritization of this new field of science.

In 1991, Dr. Heinz Gerischer, the former director of the Max Planck Institute for Physical Chemistry, spoke to German universities and government agencies. Robert Bass described Gerischer's awakening to the reality of cold fusion in a 1994 letter: "Gerischer is generally regarded as Europe's leading electrochemist. A dedicated and articulate foe of cold fusion in the very beginning, Gerischer was invited to present a summary address at the conclusion of the 2nd International Cold Fusion Conference in Como, Italy, in 1991. This forced him to study the evidence. His concluding address was equivocal, but after he got back to Germany, he circulated among the German universities and government a private letter:

> In spite of my earlier conclusions that the phenomena reported by Fleischmann and Pons in 1989 either depend on measurement errors or were of chemical origin, there is now undoubtedly overwhelming indications that nuclear processes take place in metal alloys. ... I consider it absolutely necessary that these phenomena are systematically researched. ... The fact that, in the Republic of

Germany, this work has been inhibited is no more justified. It could later on be regarded as a very unfortunate gap in German research when compared with the activity in other countries and particularly in Japan.[1]

In the United States, during the 1989 congressional hearings in which funding for cold fusion was discussed, Ira Magaziner, a business consultant who later became an adviser to the Clinton administration, eloquently alerted the U.S. Congress to his concern:

I am here because I am concerned about my three children and the future prosperity of their generation in America.

American scientists at RCA invented the color television, but today European and East Asian companies produce over 97 percent of the world's color televisions, including 85 percent of those bought by Americans. American scientists at AT&T Bell Labs and Texas Instruments invented the base technology that produced the world's first memory chip, but today Japanese companies produce over 80 percent of the world's memory chips including over 50 percent of those bought by American companies.

Suppose that this science is real and it does open up a new energy source in the next decade and becomes a multibillion- dollar or even hundred-billion-dollar industry in the next few decades. If we dawdle and wait until the science is proven and if we wait for the economists to hold symposia on whether Adam Smith would approve of putting public money into it or if we move cautiously and invest only in basic research or only in defense applications and wait for the spin-off, we will be much slower off the blocks than our Japanese and European competitors, because they won't run the race that way.

The United States currently lags behind Japan in cold fusion research. It is also formidably challenged by China's strong theoretical work and existing thin-film metal plating industry, by Russia's large, inexpensive scientific labor pool, by the enthusiastic support for this new science seen in various Italian agencies, and by Israel's heavy private investment in cold fusion research.

240

While little has heretofore been mentioned of the Israeli cold fusion effort, in 2003, several researchers from a well-funded Israeli company stunned the cold fusion community with their results. They also angered people by withholding their methods, clearly to preserve their commercial advantage.

Magaziner concluded his impassioned speech by expressing his hopes for America:

> I have an interest in America's future. I see this as an opportunity for America both to develop this science into future American prosperity and to develop a model for how America can regain world pre-eminence in commercializing other new sciences in the coming decade.
>
> I have come here today to ask you to prevent another TV or VCR or computerized machine tool or solar cell or superconductor story. I have come to ask you to lead, so that we will not be the first of our nation's 10 generations to leave our children a country less prosperous than the one we inherited. I have come here to ask you, for the sake of my children and all of America's next generation, to have America do it right this time.[2]

Relative to Magaziner's concerns, United States citizens should consider what it might mean for them and for the global economic structure that any country, including Japan, China or Israel, might advance in cold fusion research at a much faster rate than the United States. When the U.S. Patent and Trademark Office lifts its ban on cold fusion, a foreseeable event, what will be the consequences? In the United States and in much of the free, developed world, the owner of a U.S. patent, no matter in which country the owner lives, holds exclusive rights to produce, market and sell products based on the specific patented technology. Anyone wishing to engage in business using that specific technology must pay royalties or licensing fees to the patent holder. Foreign companies and agencies that have cold fusion patent applications pending in the United States will be the ones to reap the rewards, ... whether U.S. researchers are just one year or one day behind researchers in other countries.

Threats to International Security

Although no public information indicates that low energy nuclear reactions have weapons capacity, the theoretical possibility exists.

There is a significant distinction between an energy source used for power consumption and an energy source used for weaponry. An energetic weapon requires a rapid rate of energy release; this is the essence of a bomb. Alternatively, a power-generating device, such as the burning of a piece of coal, requires a moderate rate of energy release. By all known accounts, cold fusion consistently demonstrates a moderate rate of energy release, which would be ideal for power consumption if it can be scaled up.

The fact that cold fusion experiments, on occasion, do evolve tritium suggests the potential for an application to conventional nuclear weapons. In the closing comments of the 9th International Conference on Cold Fusion, McKubre said, "Sadly, in all of this, we have tritium production. This is another thing that I resisted, the notion that tritium is being produced in these experiments. Tritium production is absolutely unambiguously clearly produced. ... And tritium is a product that has value and use - not good uses, in most cases."

Tritium is a key component in the triggering mechanism of nuclear warheads. Even if new warheads are never produced, existing weapons need regular replenishment of tritium. Tritium decays quickly, with a half-life of 12.5 years. The only other known source for tritium production is nuclear fission reactors, which are neither simple nor inexpensive to build and maintain. No one knows whether cold fusion will produce sufficient quantities of tritium for weapons sustainment and replenishment.

One of the world's top experts on tritium in cold fusion experiments works at Los Alamos National Laboratory. Although he didn't want to be quoted directly, he did offer insights on the status of the topic.

He stated that, although a series of experiments performed at Los Alamos several years ago showed an impressive 50:1 signal-to-noise ratio, he has stopped performing experiments. At best, he said, they were able to achieve only a 20 percent rate of reproducibility. For now, they have halted the experiments so they can better understand the metallurgical properties of the few cathodes that worked. "Until we finish analyzing it," he said, "attempting to use cold fusion as a reliable mechanism to produce tritium seems unlikely, based on current success. We'd be spinning our wheels to continue with new attempts."[3]

Another cold fusion researcher, who works for a Department of Defense contractor and who spoke anonymously, expressed displeasure with the U.S. government neglecting to take cold fusion seriously:

> Lets face it, if [low energy nuclear reaction] studies make it easy to produce cold fusion someday (in a clean form), it may also be easy to "tweak it" into [ways] that produce [weapons], too. This fact cannot be ignored any longer. If so, who will accept the social consequences? Who will watch out for the public safety if such new forms of energy are made possible in simple means? Some might feel I'm being reactionary, and it might cause [this] research to be "squelched" from public view, but until we know what is and is not possible, we must proceed with caution and consider the possible ramifications. There are tradeoffs in any new technology, safety issues being one of them that must be considered.[4]

This researcher made the point that critical junctures before society and government can influence the direction of cold fusion research for many decades. Because the capacity for weapons eventually may be confirmed, those in the position to do so at this time must set in place courses of action that focus research on peaceful and benevolent uses for cold fusion technology.

CHAPTER THIRTY-ONE

Lessons Learned

Brian Josephson, a Nobel prize-winning physicist, has taken the initiative to evaluate cold fusion theories and witness working cold fusion cells. Writing to a critic of cold fusion in a June 2004 e-mail, he said:

> In regard to cold fusion, it would be advisable for the scientific community to brace itself for the fallout that will be coming soon when the public starts to become aware that the scientific community was engaging in an act of gross self-deception back in 1989.

Who is to blame for the neglect and delay of serious research and development in a field that apparently holds such immense promise for humankind?

Charles Beaudette eloquently summarized this poignant issue by using a metaphor of a 100-milliliter test tube to apportion the blame for cold fusion being relegated, as he put it, into a scientific ghetto.

The majority of the blame, as he saw it, stems from the events at the May 1-3, 1989, Baltimore American Physical Society presentations and press conferences:

> The presentations get 30 milliliters for the comprehensive errors in descriptions of Fleischmann and Pons' experiment and of the two chemists' persons. The claim that Fleischmann and Pons were incompetent and mentally ailing was unethical as well as wrong.

The four press conferences also get 30 milliliters for their intense, aggressive purpose and for their successful impact. The assertion of "absolute" knowledge that was offered to the cream of the nation's science reporters was a knowing attack. The further assertion that the Caltech experiments were more sophisticated than those done in Utah was unnecessary as well as wrong. The four press conferences turned the scientific community away from its duty to evaluate what was claimed and redirected its interest to the mean practice of politics.

The Baltimore attacks not only destroyed Fleischmann and Pon's reputation but also set in place a stern warning for other scientists who dared to keep an open mind:

This climate of fear was put into place at Baltimore by the mistaken attack on Fleischmann and Pons ... and by the savage and ignorant criticism of their calorimetry. After those eminently successful attacks, who else dared to risk suffering from such public ruthlessness?

Beaudette apportioned 20 milliliters of blame to *Nature* magazine for failing to publish Oriani's confirmation of the Fleischmann-Pons effect in 1990.

The University of Utah administration got 10 milliliters for placing its self-interests of greed and fame ahead of a scientific ethic that would have placed a higher value on thoroughness, disclosure and precision.

And finally, Beaudette apportioned to Fleischmann and Pons themselves, 10 milliliters for their errors with nuclear measurements, among other things:

I accept that they had a tiger by the tail and no way to let go. They were inexperienced in matters of public communication. A part of their science was in error. They ought to have renounced that data promptly, and it was wrong that they did not share cell data with their colleagues at the university.

How is it that the behavior of respected scientists who are regarded as objective, dispassionate seekers of truth could have degenerated so deplorably? "It's helpful to remember," Dr. David R. Hawkins wrote in his book, *Power vs. Force: The Hidden Determinants of Human Behavior*, "that it's a foible of human nature to stoutly defend an established position despite overwhelming evidence against it."

Perhaps it is time for modern science to reconsider its tendency to rely heavily on theory and little on empirical experience. As Professor Emeritus William S. Gaud wrote, "nature's reality is always the final judge of a scientific theory." [1]

Misinformation about cold fusion has pervaded the educational system. This too, needs to change. Over the last 15 years, the cold fusion episode has been used as a prime example of science gone awry and, worse yet, the single most-cited example of pathological science in college-level science ethics courses.

Physics Professor John Cotton of Southern Methodist University, for example, teaches a course titled "The Scientific Method: Critical and Creative Thinking." The course description states that, "if true, [cold fusion] would be one of the most significant discoveries of the 20th century." It also says, "This course will introduce you to pseudo-science, outlandish claims, hype and outright BS. ... Expect to do a lot of reading, writing and, most of all, thinking."

Can Cotton be faulted for his misunderstandings? Probably not. His line of questioning relies on the misinformation supplied by cold fusion's opponents. He asks, "A hoax? Probably not. Hoax implies deliberate deception. Threshold phenomenon? They were using instruments to record their data. Scientific error? Seems most likely. ... They were electrochemists working in physics, which meant they were working out of their area of expertise." [2]

Likewise, can he be faulted for the misconception that cold fusion resulted from shoddy science or from chemists working outside of their field of expertise, when most evidence to the contrary was effectively suppressed or not yet revealed?

Further answers to how so many have been so misinformed come from Beaudette, who pointed out that the authors of anti-cold fusion books failed in their responsibility to report the full story to the world:

In America, to hide important information from the public is now referred to as a cover-up. When the excess heat did not disappear with the introduction of precise calorimetry [as the skeptics predicted], skeptical physicists adopted cover-up behavior toward it. Huizenga's book omitted references to the topic for occurrences after June 1989. Frank Close did not include [any] such references in his book. ... The skeptics did not [even] say that the excess heat measurements were inadequate; they simply ignored them as though the laboratory work did not exist and the scientists doing that work were dead. ... No cover-up like this has happened before. It is a profound scandal in American science.[3]

Truth prevailing, in the final chapter of history, cold fusion will be known as both a tragic and a classic example of mankind's resistance to new ideas. It also will be known for the miraculous struggle and revival of a scientific effort that was neglected and nearly lost, moments before its final breath.

This future remains to be seen. The documented evidence and written instructions by the mostly retired scientists in the cold fusion field are not enough to carry this knowledge forward. Every scientist who has been working in the cold fusion field must be given the opportunity to disseminate accumulated knowledge and experience to the younger generations. There is no substitute for the direct interaction of teacher and student.

The premature burial of cold fusion was exemplified no more clearly than by Sir John Maddox, editor of the prestigious British journal *Nature*:

I think that, broadly speaking, it's dead. And it will remain dead for a long, long time. [4]

Broadly speaking, Maddox was mistaken, and he will remain mistaken, for a long, long time. The world will have to accept the awakening interest of the nation's youth, who have been downloading cold fusion papers from www.lenr-canr.org by the tens of thousands.

248

CHAPTER THIRTY-TWO

Speculation About the Future

Power Density

At some point, cold fusion will be understood well enough by scientists to consider its potential commercial applications. Clearly, cold fusion at the present time is merely a scientific curiosity. The production of one watt of thermal power does nothing to solve humankind's energy problems or, for that matter, to light the smallest light bulb. However, cold fusion is at the very beginning of what is likely to be an historic scientific and technological development, and great discoveries often appear insignificant without imagination and foresight.

For example, the Wright brothers' monumental 59-second flight on Dec. 17, 1903, was not practical in any regard; however, it unequivocally demonstrated the concept of a discovery that changed nearly every aspect of the world. Thomas Edison's first light bulb, which initially lasted a mere 13 hours, was wholly impractical; however, this too demonstrated a novel discovery that was also to change the world.

Lest we forget, they, too, had their critics:

"Flight by machines heavier than air is unpractical and insignificant, if not utterly impossible," said Simon Newcomb, a mathematician and astronomer. And *The New York Times* wrote on Jan. 16, 1880, "after a few more flashes in the pan, we shall hear very little more of Edison or his electric lamp. Every claim he makes has been tested and proved impracticable."

One of the major parameters which will indicate whether cold fusion will ever become a practical source of energy is called power density. The next few pages will present information suitable for more technical readers. Content suitable for general readers will resume in the section Commercial Applications. Professor David Nagel provided a summary of the key parameters which relate to cold fusion's usefulness:

> From an engineering viewpoint, from a practical viewpoint, there is a clear list of parameters in terms of performance that are important to consider relative to the potential usefulness of cold fusion. Power density is an important one because it sizes the power-generating device. Other key factors include the total energy that can be delivered, the ability to turn it on, turn it off, the temperature it runs at. Like one's automobile, all these factors are important. The controllability aspect of it determines the performance and therefore the utility of a machine." [1]

Will a cold fusion reactor require the space of a three-story building just to provide enough electricity to power a toaster oven? Or will the inverse be the case? This is the concept of power density. It is a critical factor in determining the various practical applications of any energy source. Power density will determine cold fusion's application potential for both fixed locations, such as homes, and mobile locations, such as cars and cargo trucks. Based on the relatively high power densities observed so far, cold fusion shows every indication of having the potential for sufficient power density for each of these applications.

Figure 4-1 shows a progression of some of the more powerful cold fusion experiments on record and compares those values to the 500 to 1,000 watts per cubic centimeter that are typically obtained from the fuel rods of conventional nuclear reactors. An earlier version of this chart was created by Nagel while he was at the U.S. Naval Research Laboratory.

The first point on the graph is from the original Fleischmann and Pons 1989 paper, published in the *Journal of Electroanalytical Chemistry*. They wrote that the excess heat exceeded "10 watts per cubic centimeter of the palladium electrode" and that this rate of power was "maintained for experimental times in excess of 120 hours, during which, typically, heat in excess of 4 mega-joules per cubic centimeter of [the palladium] electrode volume was

250

liberated." They concluded, "It is inconceivable that this could be due to anything but nuclear processes." [2]

The second point on the graph is from Fleischmann and Pons' paper published in *Physics Letters A* which describes a set of four cold fusion cells that boiled dry, even *after* the input power was turned off. The experiment was documented using time-lapse video and was shown at the 3rd International Conference on Cold Fusion, in Nagoya, Japan. The paper identifies the "excess rate of energy production" at 3,700 watts per cubic centimeter, which they note is, "broadly speaking, in line with those achieved in fast breeder [nuclear fission] reactors." [3]

The third point is based on a paper by Italian physicist Giuliano Preparata. As reported by Beaudette, Fleischmann spoke of the remarkable power density reported by Preparata at the October 1999 American Chemical Society session on cold fusion in Ontario, California:

> [Preparata's experiments] regularly get heat [density] releases of 10 kilowatts per cubic centimeter and occasionally 100 kilowatts per cubic centimeter. If this can be done reliably, this would allow one to construct systems that would satisfy a large portion of the world's energy needs with existing palladium production.

COLD FUSION VOLUMETRIC POWER DENSITIES

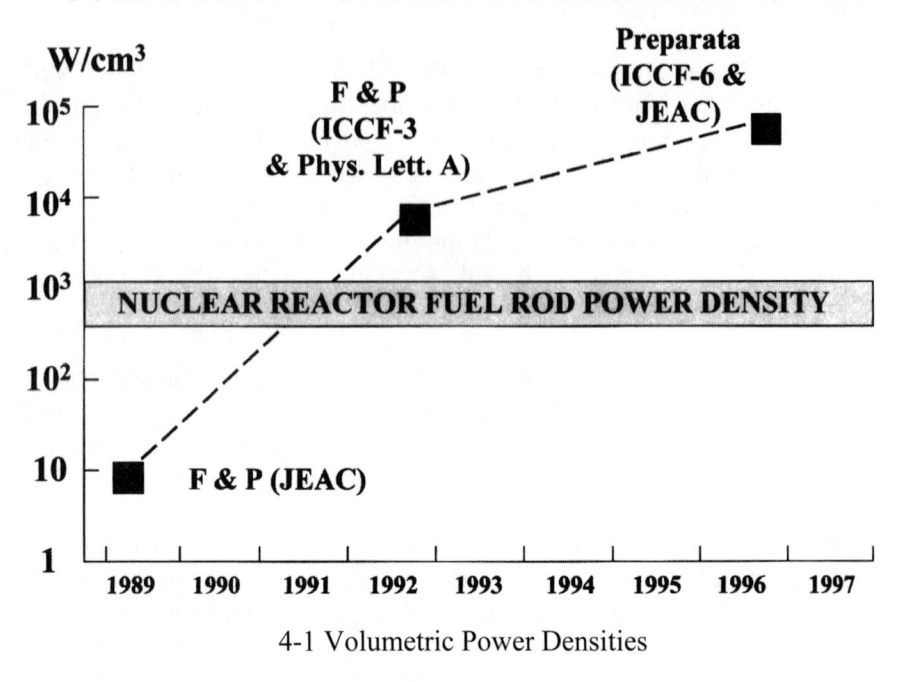

4-1 Volumetric Power Densities

In Preparata's paper, published in the *Journal of Electroanalytical Chemistry*, he noted that the experiments ran over tens of hours and that these results were "observed in about 50 similar experiments."[4]

In 2004, Fleischmann reflected further on Preparata and his accomplishments:

> He saw it very clearly, when we talked about cold fusion; I pointed out to him that the real thing one had to do was to combine cold fusion with migration of deuterons in the lattice. And he picked this up good and hard and developed this. The full glory of this is in the work that Antonella De Ninno reported. That is the paper by Giuliano Preparata, Emilio Del Guidice, Antonella De Ninno and [physicist] Antonio Fratollilo. Preparata made many enemies, too. He didn't suffer fools gladly - and there are many fools.

I think their work at the Agency for New Technology, Energy and Environment in Frascati, a nuclear research facility in Italy, is the most remarkable work. What they did is they saw very high energy release, which led to the melting of the metal. [This implies a temperature of 1,800 Celsius for the palladium.] And people will say, "Oh, it fused because you put too much power in electrically." But of course, that is not so. It is a totally inadequate explanation. The power put in electrically is orders of magnitude too small to melt the wire from any ordinary means. The other thing they showed was, when they had excess heat, they got helium-4. They did very good mass spectroscopy on it, so I regard that as a key paper.[5]

De Ninno, too, expressed great admiration for Preparata:

He was, at times, a controversial figure in high energy physics. In addition to his success in Italy, he was also a member of the theoretical division at CERN [the world's largest particle physics laboratory] and had been a visiting scientist at Princeton and Harvard. His reputation as a physicist was never questioned, but rather, his personality became a subject of controversy, because it was said that he was far too aggressive and conceited, though this was not my experience of him.[6]

Ed Storms provided an interesting alternative view on the matter of power density. Storms said that the raw power density of the actual material (palladium or other metal) eventually may be shown to be much greater than all of the values depicted in this chart. "From a materials perspective, it's very difficult to know exactly what the true power density will really turn out to be," he said. He was critical of all of these studies because the entire volume of palladium was used to calculate the power density values. In more recent years, some researchers have determined that the cold fusion phenomenon is a *surface effect* of the metal, rather than a *bulk effect*, so the true power density may turn out to be much higher if the active portion of the palladium turns out to be exclusive to just the outer surface of the material. Storms said the following:

We know that there are isolated regions on the palladium where the excess heat effect occurs. We know that they are probably in the micron to nano-meter size. We don't know how much volume is associated with a typical cell that is producing heat. The only thing you can measure is the physical volume of the entire cathode, and that's of course what was used during the early analysis [as described above]. The density is high enough to melt the palladium occasionally, so we know the density has to be really extraordinary in [hot spots]. But the big practical question is how high a power density can be obtained from an engineering point of view. This cannot yet be determined."

Storms acknowledged that the surface versus bulk effect is still hotly debated within the cold fusion community, though he believes that sufficient evidence has been presented.[7]

Commercial Applications

According to Sir Arthur C. Clarke, the future of cold fusion is unknown but hopeful:

The question is, What effect will this have on our society in the future? Well, it's just possible [these effects] may be no more than laboratory curiosities and can't be scaled up to commercial levels. I think that's rather unlikely. Nuclear energy was once a laboratory curiosity. So let's assume that these curiosities can be scaled up. The future is almost unlimited. It can be the end of the fossil fuel age, the end of oil and coal, and the end, incidentally, of many of our worries about global pollution and global warming.[8]

In a September 1996 report which culminated many years of experimentation, Dr. Melvin Miles and others at the Naval Air Warfare Center Weapons Division at China Lake, California, wrote:

In our opinion, these factors provide compelling evidence that the anomalous effects measured in deuterated systems [that is, cold fusion] are real. This research area has the potential to provide the human race with a nearly unlimited new source of energy. We hope that other scientists will continue to investigate this difficult research area until the challenging problems impeding progress are solved. It is possible that [cold fusion] will prove to be one of the most important scientific discoveries of this century.[9]

The transmutation experiments performed around the world have sparked the imagination of scientists now eager to discover whether nuclear waste might be converted, or remediated, to non-radioactive substances.

Yasuhiro Iwamura is optimistic that "nuclear reactions in condensed matter will be used for radioactive remediation" though he believes that this is quite far in the future. Alternatively, he believes that an "energy source using this phenomena would be commercialized faster."

Cold fusion scientists see several applications on the horizon. "Desalination ranks as one of the very attractive possibilities for using the energy that would be available from this kind of a power source," Nagel said. The heavy-water experiment lends itself to this possibility because, as the experiment generates excess heat, water evaporates, and its condensation results in "sweet" (pure) water. "Ten percent of the world's countries get their water from sources in other countries," he commented. "Another large fraction of countries have problems such as we do in the United States with the Colorado River. It's a very important issue."

Emphasizing the many hidden variables left to be uncovered, Nagel, addressing a maturing audience of cold fusion scientists, said that "the pressing question for many of us in the community who are not in the earliest stages of our careers is, Can we get it right soon?" [10]

Resolving the remaining issues requires additional funding as well as further breakthroughs in the field. The hot and cold fusion approaches share two challenges: they must find a way to generate enough excess power to be cost-effective, and they must overcome the science and engineering hurdles that prevent the systems from running continuously.

Those in the hot fusion field have looked long and hard at the hurdles which they must overcome before hot fusion attains commercial viability. The Lawson criterion, named after British scientist John D. Lawson, first identified the conditions needed to get close to a commercial hot fusion power system. While the Lawson criterion does not apply exactly to cold fusion, it does provide a similar framework of understanding from which to evaluate the field's proximity to usefulness.

The first breakthrough in the Lawson criterion requires that the amount of energy released from a fusion reaction equal the amount of energy going into the reaction. This has not been achieved in hot fusion but has, many times over, in cold fusion.[11] The second and third milestones in the Lawson criterion define additional levels of power generation. Only the fourth level, "commercial viability," indicates imminent practicality, when the overall cost of the entire process is cost-effective compared to other forms of energy. This relationship applies equally to cold fusion's potential as a replacement energy source.

Figure 4-2 displays a broad comparison of various characteristics of the current state of hot fusion with the state of cold fusion research.

As shown in this chart, the known characteristics of the two forms of fusion are markedly different. The paradigm of hot fusion fits in with the existing model of power generation, transmission and consumption. Large centralized plants produce large quantities of power for entire cities. The power is distributed through a grid of transmission lines and substations. The paradigm of cold fusion shows a newer model based on self-contained, localized power units that run just enough power for their respective appliances, vehicles or buildings.

Dependency on the power grid brings with it a host of problems. As was seen in the northeastern United States in the summer of 2003, catastrophic failures can occur when the power grid is poorly maintained. With a few points of failure, the consequences of a power failure also can be enormous when capacity, on a countrywide or regional basis, nears its peak, as happened in California in 2001. Alternatively, the failure of a home-based cold fusion generator would affect only that specific home. Large centralized power plants also present major security risks, because they can become targets for terrorists.

While cold fusion does not appear to generate the large-scale production capacities demonstrated by hot fusion experiments, pound for pound, it has surpassed hot fusion in several ways. In the following chart, the cold fusion

256

statistics presented are generally conservative. Papers have reported isolated instances showing higher values.

First, cold fusion experiments generate more power out than power in. This finding is ubiquitous in the cold fusion field. Second, at least four reports have shown sustained nuclear reactions after input power to the experimental cells has been turned off.

In addition to deuterium, hot fusion reactions require tritium and lithium, which are radioactive and highly toxic materials. Tritium, as well, is a highly restricted material and would never be allowed for distributed power applications. Cold fusion can run exclusively on deuterium, a harmless variant of hydrogen. This enables a far greater number of commercial applications that co-exist with normal human activity and environments.

Figure 4-2 Comparison of Hot and Cold Fusion

	Hot Fusion	Cold Fusion
Years Studied	50	15
Estimated U.S. funding to date	$16 Billion [12]	$25 Million [13]
Committed future U.S. funding	> $10 Billion	?
Experimental Qualities Shows potential for large-scale power generation	Yes	No
Shows potential for power production at point of consumption	No (too big)	Yes
Demonstrates self-sustaining nuclear reaction	Never	Yes [14]
Peak Experimental Power Levels Peak output power levels Duration	16 Megawatt 1 second	10 watts 2000 hours [15]
Ratio of power out/power in (break-even =1.0)	0.6	> 1.1 [15]
Typical Experimental Power Levels Typical excess power levels Duration	0 n/a	1 watt 5-600 hours [16]
Fuel	Deuterium + Tritium + Lithium	Deuterium
Dangerous and/or radioactive fuel	Yes	No
Commercialization Expectations Earliest estimated commercialization	2050	2010
Requires power distribution grid	Yes	No
Possible use in transportation	No	Yes
Single point of failure Security risk	Yes	No

In Their Own Words

On reflection, for those scientists who have pioneered, risked and sacrificed to journey into the mysterious unknown, cold fusion has brought thrills and perils, hope and despair. Nevertheless, from a combination of extraordinary intelligence, confidence, unwavering pursuit of scientific truth, and courage to defy prevailing thought, they have largely triumphed.

The following statements capture some of their experiences and expectations for this new field of science:

Francesco Scaramuzzi, 2002:

It is evident that this field requires a more massive effort in order to attain steady progress. Propagation of the research into the rest of the scientific community would greatly contribute to this result. ... The reasons "why" one should devote a more massive effort to develop cold fusion are clear to me, and I hope that they are convincing to you. The study of collective and coherent phenomena promises very high intellectual rewards, and the hope of contributing to the solution of the problem of the energy supply for mankind is highly inspiring. Last but not least, the challenge of studying a field which is not well understood is definitely fascinating. Albert Einstein said, "The most beautiful experience we can have is the mysterious. It is the fundamental emotion which stands at the cradle of true art and true science.[17]

Jean Paul Biberian, 1996:

It's history in the making, what we are living through here. I couldn't dream of being in a situation like this. Can you imagine living at the time of Einstein, Curie and Bohr, all these great people who were completely changing the nature of science at the beginning of the century? When I was going to college, I was told, "All the great discoveries are over now. They're done. Just shut up, and learn."

259

Now, all of a sudden, I don't have to shut up, and I can do something. I can bring my own contribution to science and society.[18]

Sir Arthur C. Clarke, 1996:

There's a curious parallel back at the beginning of the century when the Wright Brothers first flew in 1903. No newspaper covered it at all because everybody was convinced, certainly the American press, that heavier-than-air flight was totally impossible. All the top scientists said, "This is nonsense." Editors wouldn't even bother to send journalists or photographers to interview the Wrights or even to take pictures of them flying in full public view. It wasn't until about five years later that they realized, "My goodness, this is real! Heavier-than-air flight is possible." And I think a similar thing is going to happen with cold fusion.[19]

John O'Mara Bockris, 1996:

I was 69 years old at that time, and I took the attitude, "It doesn't really matter. I've had my career." The worst they could do would be to say, "Go! Your tenure is ended." And therefore, I wasn't frightened. I went on saying the truth, publishing what we got.

I think the main part was that I had done work which was against the paradigm. That was what they were really upset about. You know, people said that they had been to our university, and they laughed at them: "What the heck are you doing? Trying to disprove the laws of nuclear physics? That's exactly what we were doing, and succeeding, you see.[20]

J. Reece Roth, 2003:

Many of my colleagues are quite tenacious about existing approaches, and one example of that is their insistence on pursuing the Tokamak magnetic fusion concept rather than looking elsewhere for the optimal way of achieving fusion. ... Cold fusion may very well be capable of producing fusion energy under conditions that will make it very inexpensive and environmentally very desirable. It's entirely possible that, if cold fusion goes the way [it has been] described, everybody will be able to have their own fusion reactor in their basement, and the distributed power from electric utilities will be a thing of the past." [21]

George Miley, 1996:

We may have a new energy source which could be capable of being made in very small units on up to large units. It may revolutionize our future energy supply. Energy is still basic to man; it's basic to our standard of living. And if it's a type of energy that doesn't pollute, as we currently envision cold fusion, ... not only will this give us a future energy source but it's going to help us be good stewards of our universe. [22]

Edmund Storms, 2002:

These forthcoming technologies are very basic to the way society is organized and the way people live. They are going to change our lifestyle enormously. They're going to change how political power operates and alter the economic structure of the world. They are going to have a basic fundamental impact. They will allow mankind to live in all parts of the world, many of which are inhospitable now because water is unavailable. These energy sources will allow water to be made available from the oceans by inexpensive desalinization. They will also allow mankind to explore the universe. At the present time, we can't do that because chemical energy is not sufficiently dense and conventional nuclear energy is too dangerous. These new kinds of energy sources are sufficiently dense and don't have these other problems, so they would allow us to explore the solar system and beyond. Who knows what possibilities would come about? [23]

Krityunjai Prasad Sinha, Visiting Professor, MIT,
Fellow, India National Academy of Science
Fellow, India Academy of Science
Fellow, India National Science Academy:

I have done a lot of physics. I have published 250 papers and five books. But now I want to do useful research which is good for mankind, that is, energy production and energy transmission. My interests are anything which can give abundant energy so that each house can have its own source of energy and become self-sufficient so that it doesn't have to depend on energy transmission. I'm working on not only cold fusion but also other aspects of energy transfer and energy production. I feel that within five to 10 years the problem will be solved.[24]

Dorothy Hubler, 2004:

If cold fusion ever comes to be, which I really believe it will in the near future, people will be receiving Nobel prizes, and *that* can create a lot of envy and jealousy, too! But I think whoever does it will have the world's respect for their creativity and ingenuity. And it won't be one person; it will be a collaboration of many scientists. This is the beauty of the scientific world. They collaborate together; they work together internationally.[25]

Martin Fleischmann, 1994:

If it had been anything else, we would have said, "People don't want us to do it: Forget it. Let's just leave it alone." But this is not in that category. This is interesting science, new science, with a hint of a possibility of a very useful technology. Therefore, if you've got any integrity, you don't give it up. You give it up if you find you are wrong. But as long as you believe that you are right, you have to continue with it. And you have to take the consequences.[26]

Appendix A

University Scientists Interviewed or Cited

Dmitriy Afonichev, professor of physics, Institute for Metals Superplasticity, Russian Academy of Sciences

Yoshiaki Arata, professor of physics emeritus, Osaka University, Japan.

Jean-Paul Biberian, professor of physics, University of Luminy in Marseilles, consultant with the French Atomic Energy Commission (ret.)

John O'M Bockris, professor of electrochemistry Texas A&M University (ret.)

Robert Bush, professor of physics, California Polytechnic Institute, Pomona, California

Dan Chicea, professor of atomic and nuclear physics, University Lucian Blaga of Sibiu, Romania

Dennis Cravens, professor of chemistry and physics, Eastern New Mexico University

John Dash, professor of metallurgy and physics, Portland State University

Melvin Eisner, professor of physics, University of Houston (ret.)

Peter Hagelstein, professor of electrical engineering and computer science, MIT

Wilford Hansen, professor of chemistry and physics, Utah State University (ret.)

Andrei Lipson, professor of physics, University of Illinois, Urbana and Russian Academy of Sciences.

Xing Zhong Li, professor of theoretical nuclear physics, Tsinghua University, Beijing China.

Michael Melich, professor of physics, U.S. Naval Post-Graduate School

Melvin Miles, professor of chemistry, University of La Verne, California

George Miley, professor of Nuclear and Electrical Engineering, University of Illinois

Tadahiko Mizuno, assistant professor of nuclear engineering, Graduate School of Engineering, Hokkaido University, Japan

David Nagel, research professor, The George Washington University

Richard Oriani, professor of physical chemistry emeritus, University of Minnesota

Steven Jones, professor of physics, Brigham Young University

(Anonymous,) professor of physics, Purdue University

Ludwik Kowalski, professor of physics, Montclair State University

Hideo Kozima, professor of physics, Portland State University

J. Reece Roth, professor of fusion energy, University of Tennessee

Krityunjai Prasad Sinha, visiting professor of theoretical physicist, MIT

Akito Takahashi, chair of nuclear instrumentation, Department of Nuclear Engineering, Graduate School of Engineering, Osaka University, Japan

Appendix B

2003 Survey of Nuclear Transmutations in Cold Fusion Experiments

Hokkaido University, Japan - Mizuno et al., Notoya et al.
Mitsubishi Corporation, Japan - Iwamura et al.
Osaka University, Japan - Takahashi et al., Arata et al.
University of Leece, Italy - Vincenzo et al.
Frascati Laboratory, Italy - De Ninno et al.
SIA "LUTCH", Russia - Karabut et al., Savvatimova et al.
Tomsk Polytechnical University, Russia - Chernov et al.
Lab des Sciences Nucleaires, France - Dufour et al.
Beijing University, China - Jiang et al.
Tsinghua University, China - Li et al.
University of Illinois, Urbana, USA - Miley et al.
Portland State University, USA - Dash et al.
Texas A & M University, USA - Bockris et al.
Shizuoka University, Japan - Kozima et al.
Iwate University, Japan - Yamada et al.

Appendix C

The Scientific Process
(also known as The Scientific Method)

Text and diagram provided courtesy of William S. Gaud, Professor
Emeritus, Department of Biological Sciences, Ph.D. University of
North Carolina, based on an original diagram by Wendy Gorman

Scientists make progress by using the scientific method, a process of
checking conclusions against nature. After observing something, a scientist
tries to explain what has been seen.

The explanation is called an hypothesis. There is always at least one
alternative hypothesis.

A part of nature is tested in a "controlled experiment" to see if the
explanation matches reality. A controlled experiment is one in which all
treatments are identical except that some are exposed to the hypothetical
cause and some are not. Any differences in the way the treatments behave is
attributed to the presence and lack of the cause.

If the results of the experiment are consistent with the hypothesis, there is
evidence to support the hypothesis. If the two do not match, the scientist
seeks an alternative explanation and redesigns the experiment.

When enough evidence accumulates, the understanding of this natural
phenomenon is considered a scientific theory. A scientific theory persists
until additional evidence causes it to be revised.

Nature's reality is always the final judge of a scientific theory.

The Scientific Process (Method)

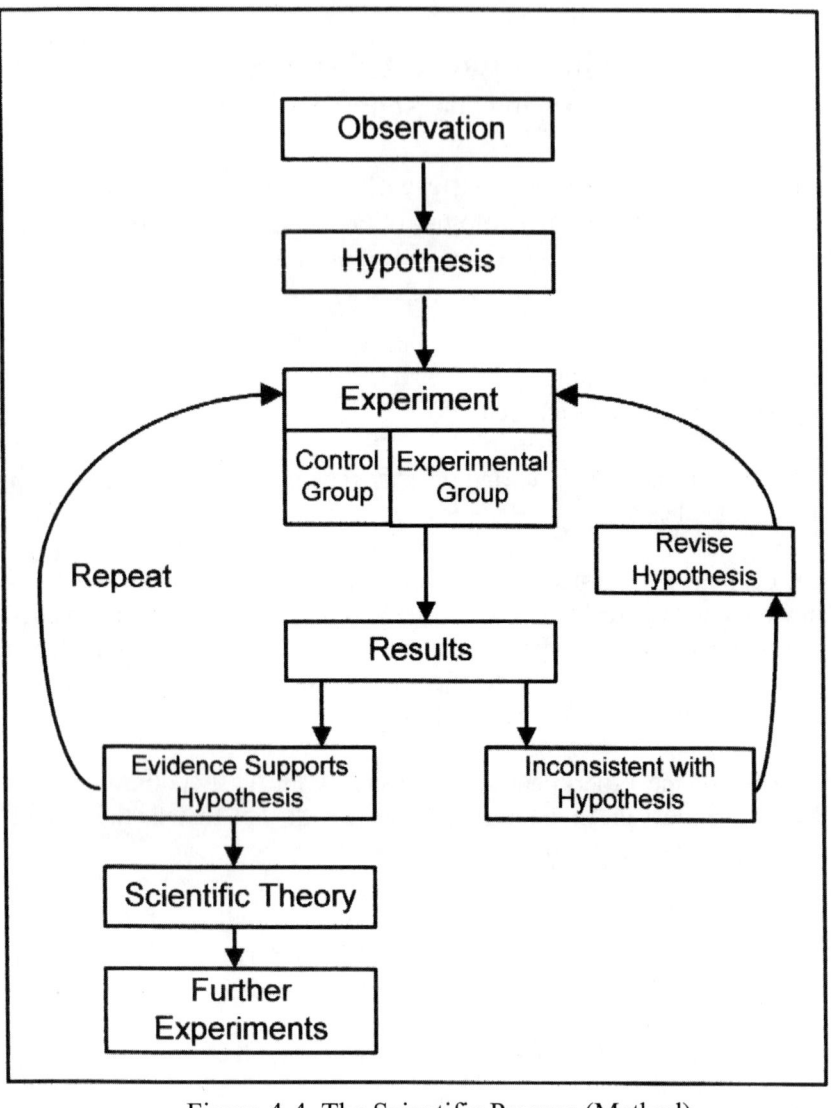

Figure 4-4. The Scientific Process (Method)

Endnotes

Chapter 1, Cold Fusion Basics

1. Nelson, Steve,
   http://www.madsci.org/posts/archives/Apr2003/1051645602.Ph.r.html
2. Storms, Edmund, private communications, (July 8, 2004)

Chapter 2, Immense Hope and Skepticism

1. Owens, Wayne, "Recent Developments in Fusion Energy Research," 101st Cong.,
   1st Ses., April 26, 1989; no. 46.

Chapter 3, Fuel Scarcity and Climate Change

1. Association for the Study of Peak Oil,
   www.hubbertpeak.com/aspo/iwood/ASPOpress_2.pdf
2. Appenzeller, Tim, "The End of Cheap Oil," National Geographic, (June 2004) p.
   80
3. Campbell, Virginia, "How RAND Invented the postwar world," *Invention and
   Technology Magazine*, (Summer 2004)
4. U.S. Department of Energy, http://www.eia.doe.gov/oiaf/ieo/pdf/0484.pdf (2004)
5. U.S. Environmental Protection Agency,
   http://yosemite.epa.gov/oar/globalwarming.nsf/content/impacts.html
6. Grossman, Daniel, "Spring Forward," Scientific American, (Jan. 2004), p. 84
7. Chang, Kenneth, "As Earth Warms, the Hottest Issue Is Energy," The New York
   Times, (Nov. 3, 2003)

Chapter 4, Nuclear Fission: A Mixed Blessing

1. Nature, 143, 239, 471 (1939)
2. Columbia University,
   http://www.columbia.edu/cu/news/vforum/01/enricoFermi_conf/index.html
3. Nature 143, 239, 471 (1939)
4. Anderson, H.L. et al., Nature 143, 470 (1939)

5. Heppenheimer, T.A., "Nuclear Power: What Went Wrong?," *Invention and Technology Magazine*, V. 18, No. 2. (Fall 2002), p. 46
6. Ibid.
7. Wood, Daniel, B., "Along nuclear reactor's path, cries of 'NIMBY'" http://www.csmonitor.com/2003/1204/p03s01-ussc.html
8. Heppenheimer, T.A., "Nuclear Power: What Went Wrong?," *Invention and Technology Magazine*, V. 18, No. 2. (Fall 2002), p. 46
9. Lovelock, James (as quoted by Kirsten, Aiken), "Environmentalist says nuclear energy the answer to global warming," Australian Broadcasting Company, http://www.abc.net.au/am/content/2004/s1115187.htm, (May 25, 2004)

Chapter 5, The Overextended Promise of Hot Fusion

1. Nuclear Industry Association, "Radioactivity; Fission and Fusion; and Nuclear Energy," http://www.niauk.org/article_10.shtml
2. Calculations performed by Melvin Miles
3. DeMeo, Anthony R., private communications, (June 24, 2004)
4. Domenici, Pete, (as quoted by Hoffman, Ian), " Congress could dim laser," Tri-Valley Herald, (March 27, 2004)
5. "Power of the Strongest Laser," http://hypertextbook.com/facts/1999/LizaLi.shtml
6. Nagel, David, private communications, (July 30, 2004)
7. Park, Robert, private communications, (Nov. 12, 2003)
8. Franz, Judy, (as quoted by Dee Ann Divis), "DOE's Basic Research Gets a Boost," *Tech News World*, (Aug. 22 2004)

Chapter 6, The Limited Promise of Hydrogen

1. "Fuel Cells Hit Home," *Technology Review*, (July/Aug 2004), p. 24
2. Wang, Matthew, "Questions about the Hydrogen Economy," *Scientific American*, (May 2004), p. 66
3. U.S. Department of Energy, http://www.eia.doe.gov/oiaf/ieo/pdf/0484(2004).pdf

Chapter 7, The Distant Promise of Exotic New Energies

1. Feynman, Richard, APS Meeting at Caltech, http://www.zyvex.com/nanotech/feynman.html)

2. Smalley, Richard, (as quoted by Herrera, Stephan), "Prof. Smalley's Latest Big Idea: Nano-Energy Will Save the Earth," Small Times, (Aug. 28, 2002)
3. Smalley, Richard, (as quoted by Fairley, Peter), "Solar Cell Rollout," MIT Technology Review, (July/Aug 2004), p. 34
4. Puthoff, Hal, (as quoted by Scott,William B.), *Aviation Week & Space Technology*, (Mar. 1, 2004), p. 50
5. Goldes, Mark, private communications, (June 8, 2004)
6. Rothwell, Jed, private communications, (June 8, 2004)
7. Johnson, Steven, private communications, (June 8, 2004)
8. Storms, Edmund, private communications, (July 7, 2004)
9. Taleyarkhan, Rusi P., et al., "Evidence for Nuclear Emissions During Acoustic Cavitation," *Science Magazine*, V. 295, (March 2002), p. 186
10. Chubb, Scott, private communications, (Mar. 4, 2004)
11. Stringham, Roger, private communications, (Jul. 21, 2004)
12. Storms, Edmund, private communications, (Aug 15, 2004)
13. Stringham, Roger, private communications, (Jul. 21, 2004)
14. Lipson, Andrei, G., et al., "Observation of neutrons accompanying cavitation in deuterium containing media, "*Soviet Technical Physics Letters*, 16(10), (1990), p. 763. Translated by AIP # 0360-120X/90/10 0763-02, Lipson, Andrei, G., et al., "Generation of nuclear fusion products by combined action of cavitation and electrolysis of titanium surface in deuterated electrolyte," *Technical Physics Letters*, 38(7), (1993), p. 623
15. Lipson, Andrei, private communications, (Mar 4, 2004)
16. Storms, Edmund, private communications, (Mar. 4, 2004)

Chapter 8, An Overdue Revolution in Science

1. Corey, James, "Energetic Materials: History of and Current Claims for Low Energy Nuclear Reactions," 2003 Energetic Materials Intelligence Symposium, (Sept. 10-12, 2003)
2. Nagel, David, private communications, (Feb. 11, 2004)
3. Takahashi, Akito, private communications, (Sept. 18, 2003)
4. Corey, James, "Energetic Materials: History of and Current Claims for Low Energy Nuclear Reactions," *2003 Energetic Materials Intelligence Symposium,* (Sept. 10-12, 2003)
5. Krivit, Steven, data collected from ICCF-10 abstracts, http://www.newenergytimes.com/ICCF10/iccf10.htm
6. Miley, George, private communications, (Nov. 22, 2003)
7. Storms, Edmund, private communications, (Feb. 22, 2002)
8. Storms, Edmund, "When Will We Learn to Listen?," http://www.newenergytimes.com/Conversations/storms/whenWillWeLearn.htm, (March 2002)

Chapter 9, The Moment of Discovery

1. Fleischmann, Martin, private communications, (Aug. 19. 2004)
2. Fleischmann, Martin, (as reported by Tinsley, Chris), http://www.infinite-energy.com/iemagazine/issue11/fleishmann.html
3. Bockris, John O'M., *Accountability in Research, 2000. 8* (2002), p. 59
4. Mallove, Eugene, *Fire from Ice: Searching for the Truth Behind the Cold Fusion Furor*, Infinite Energy Press, Bow, New Hampshire
5. Pons, Stanley, private communications, (Aug. 29, 2004)
6. Ashley, Kevin, private communications, (June 28, 2004)
7. Fleischmann, Martin, private communications, (Aug. 24, 2003)
8. Fleischmann, Martin, private communications, (July 19 2004)
9. Fleischmann, Martin, private communications, (April 6, 2004)
10. Beaudette, Charles, *Excess Heat & Why Cold Fusion Research Prevailed, 2nd ed.*, South Bristol, Maine, Oak Grove Press, (2002), p. 12
11. Fleischmann, M., S. Pons, and M. Hawkins, Electrochemically induced nuclear fusion of deuterium. Journal of Electroanalytical Chemistry, V.261, (1989), p. 301 and errata in Vol. 263
12. Peterson, Chase, (as quoted by Huizenga, John R.), Cold Fusion, The Scientific Fiasco of the Century, New York, Oxford University Press, (1993), p. 55
13. Storms, Edmund, private communications, (July 15, 2004)
14. Bockris, John, private communications, (May 5, 2004)
15. Fleischmann, Martin, private communications, (Aug 24, 2003)
16. Pons, Stanley and Sheila, "Too Close to the Sun" (BBC Horizon/CBC) (March 21, 1994)

Chapter 10, Con-Fusion

1. Bush, Robert, (in video by Mallove, Eugene), "Cold Fusion: Fire from Water," (1996)
2. Goodstein, David, "Whatever Happened to Cold Fusion?" Accountability in Research, 2000. 8 (2002), p. 59
3. McKubre, Michael, "RADIO WEST," (by Douglas Fubbrezio), *KUER/PBS, a service of the University of Utah KUER,* (Nov. 27, 2002)

Chapter 11, Ridicule and Violent Opposition

1. Mallove, Eugene, "MIT Special Report," *Infinite Energy, 1999 4(24),* (1999), p. 64, also at www.infinite-energy.com
2. Happer, William (as quoted by Taubes, Gary), *Bad Science: The Short Life and Weird Times of Cold Fusion*, (New York, Random House, June 15, 1993), p. 305
3. Hubler, Dorothy, private communications, (June 28, 2004)
4. Lewis, Nathan, (in video by Mallove, Eugene), "Cold Fusion: Fire from Water," (1996)
5. Bockris, John, private communications, (May 5, 2004)
6. Koonin, Steven, (as quoted by Charles Beaudette), *Excess Heat & Why Cold Fusion Research Prevailed, 2nd ed.*, South Bristol, Maine, Oak Grove Press, (2002), p. 79
7. *Ibid.*, p. 74, also Taubes, G., *Bad Science, the Short Life and Weird Times of Cold Fusion,* New York, Random House, (1993)
8. Goodstein, David, "Whatever Happened to Cold Fusion?" Accountability in Research, 2000. 8: p. 59.
9. Koonin, Steven, (as quoted by Taubes, Gary), *Bad Science: The Short Life and Weird Times of Cold Fusion*, (New York, Random House, June 15, 1993), pg 265
10. Hubler, Dorothy, private communications, (Aug. 25, 2003)

Chapter 12, A Biased 1989 Review Panel

1. Huizenga, John R., *Cold Fusion, The Scientific Fiasco of the Century*, New York, Oxford University Press, (1993), p. 297
2. Ramsey, Norman, in the preamble to "Report of the Energy Research Advisory Board to the United States Department of Energy," *http://www.ncas.org/erab* (Nov. 1989)
3. Passell, Thomas, private communications, (Jan. 6, 2004) and Passell, Thomas, (in video by Mallove, Eugene), "Cold Fusion: Fire from Water," (1996)
4. Anonymous source, private communications, (Nov. 4, 2003)

Chapter 13, False Debunking

1. Pons, Stanley, (as quoted by JoAnn Jacobsen-Wells), "U.S. Fusion Panel Cancels Plans to View University Research" *Deseret News*, (May 28, 1989)
2. Miles, Melvin, et al., "Calorimetric Principles and Problems in Pd-D2O Electrolysis, The Third International Conference on Cold Fusion," Nagoya, Japan:, Universal Academy Press, Inc., Tokyo: (1991), p. 113

3. Noninski, V.C. and Noninski, C.I., "Comments on 'measurement and analysis of neutron and gamma-ray emission rates, other fusion products, and power in electrochemical cells having palladium cathodes,' Fusion Technology, Vol. 19, (1991), p. 579

4. Melich, Michael E. and Hansen, W.N., "Some Lessons from 3 Years of Electrochemical Calorimetry, "Third International Conference on Cold Fusion," Nagoya Japan: Universal Academy Press, Inc. (1992)

5. Noninski, V.C. and Noninski, C.I., "Notes on Two Papers Claiming No Evidence for the Existence of Excess Energy During the Electrolysis of 0.1 M LiOD/D2O with Palladium Cathodes," Fusion Technology, Vol.23, (July 1993,) p. 474

6. Miles, Melvin, et al., "Correlation of excess power and helium production during D2O and H2O electrolysis using palladium cathodes," Journal of Electroanalytical Chemistry, Vol. 346, (1993), p. 99   Also similarly published 1994, Fusion Technology, Vol. 25, (1994), p. 478

7. Swartz, Mitchell, "Some Lessons from Optical Examination of the PFC Phase-II Calorimetric Curves, Vol. 2," Fourth International Conference on Cold Fusion, sponsored by EPRI and the Office of Naval Research, December (1993)

8. Melich, Michael E. and Hansen, W.N., "Back to the Future, The Fleischmann-Pons Effect in 1994," Fourth International Conference on Cold Fusion, Lahaina, Maui: Electric Power Research Institute, (1993)

9. Miles, Melvin, et al., "Calorimetric principles and problems in measurements of excess power during Pd-D2O electrolysis," Journal of Physical Chemistry, Vol. 98, (1994), p. 194

10. Miles, M., et al., "Calorimetric Principles and Problems in Measurements of Excess Power during Pd-D2O Electrolysis," *J. Phys. Chem., Vol. 98*, (1994), p. 1948

11. Melich, Michael, private communications, (Oct. 12, 2003)

12. Melich, Michael, private communications, (Oct. 13, 2003)

13. Melich, Michael E., and Hansen, Wilford, N., "Back to the Future, The Fleischmann-Pons Effect in 1994," *Fourth International Conference on Cold Fusion, Lahaina, Maui: Electric Power Research Institute 3412 Hillview Ave., Palo Alto, CA 94304,* (1993)

14. Hansen, Wilford, N. and Melich, Michael, E., "Pd/D Calorimetry - The Key to the F/P Effect and a Challenge to Science," *Fourth International Conference on Cold Fusion, Lahaina, Maui: Electric Power Research Institute 3412 Hillview Ave., Palo Alto, CA 94304,* (1993), and *Transactions of Fusion Technology, Vol. 26, Number 4T, Part 2,* (December 1994), p. 355

15. Melich, Michael, private communications, (Oct. 13, 2003), also "Reasonable doubt," (as quoted by Bennett Daviss), *New Scientist, Vol. 177, issue 2388,* (March 29, 2003), p. 36

16. Huizenga, John R., *Cold Fusion, The Scientific Fiasco of the Century*, New York, Oxford University Press, (1993), p. 297

272

17. Melich, Michael E., and Hansen, Wilford, N., "Back to the Future, The Fleischmann-Pons Effect in 1994," *Fourth International Conference on Cold Fusion. Lahaina, Maui: Electric Power Research Institute 3412 Hillview Ave., Palo Alto, CA 94304,* (1993)
18. Melich, Michael, private communications, (Oct. 13, 2003)
19. Lewis, Nathan, (as quoted by Taubes, Gary), Bad Science, the Short Life and Weird Times of Cold Fusion, New York, Random House, (1993) pg 265
20. Fleischmann, Martin, private communications, (July 15, 2004)
21. Bass, Robert, private communications, (Jan 17, 1994)
22. Lindley, David, "Letter to Noninski," (May 3, 1991)
23. Miles, Melvin, "Letter to John Maddox", (Dec. 5, 1991)
24. Miles, Melvin, et al., "Calorimetric Principles and Problems in Pd-D2O Electrolysis," The Third International Conference on Cold Fusion, Nagoya, Japan, Universal Academy Press, Inc., Tokyo, (1991), p. 113, also Miles, M., et al., "Calorimetric principles and problems in measurements of excess power during Pd-D2O electrolysis," Journal of Physical Chemistry, Vol. 98, (1994), p. 1948
25. McKubre, Michael, private communications, (Jan. 15, 2004)
26. Miles, Melvin, et al., "Correlation of excess power and helium production during D2O and H2O electrolysis using palladium cathodes," Journal of Electroanalytical Chemistry, V. 346: (1993), p. 99   Also similarly published 1994, Fusion Technology, V. 25, (1994), p. 478
27. Miles, Melvin, private communications, (Dec. 11, 2003)

Chapter 14, MIT's Fumbled (or Worse) Experiments

1. Parker, Ronald, as quoted in "MIT Bombshell Knocks Fusion 'Breakthrough' Cold," Boston Herald, May 1, 1989)
2. Mallove, Eugene, " Cold Fusion," 21st Century Radio, April 18, 2004)
3. Mallove, Eugene, "MIT Special Report," Infinite Energy, 4(24), (1999), p. 64
4. Swartz, Mitchell, "Some Lessons from Optical Examination of the PFC Phase-II Calorimetric Curves" Vol. 2, Proceedings: "Fourth International Conference on Cold Fusion," sponsored by EPRI and the Office of Naval Research, (1993)
5. Mallove, Eugene, "MIT Special Report," (Infinite Energy, 4(24), (1999)
6. Mallove, Eugene, "Cold Fusion: Fire from Water," (1996)
7. Mallove, Eugene, "MIT and Cold Fusion- A Special Report," http://www.infinite-energy.com/images/pdfs/mitcfreport.pdf
8. Ibid.
9. Swartz, Mitchell, *Fusion and Other Nuclear Reactions in the Solid State*, Jet Technology Press, Wellesley Hills, Mass. (May 1999)
10. Swartz, Mitchell, private communications, (Aug. 30, 2004)

11. Swartz, Mitchell, "Some Lessons from Optical Examination of the PFC Phase-II Calorimetric Curves," Fusion Facts, (1992)
12. Swartz, Mitchell, "Cold Fusion," 21st Century Radio, (April 18, 2004)
13. Swartz, Mitchell, private communications, (Aug 18, 2004)
14. Storms, Edmund, private communications, (Jan. 1, 2004)
15. Swartz, Mitchell, private communications, (Aug 18, 2004)

Chapter 15, Corroborating Evidence

1. Oriani, Richard, A. et al., "Calorimetric Measurements of Excess Power Output During the Cathodic Charging of Deuterium into Palladium," Fusion Technology, 1990. 18: (1990) p. 652.
2. Hansen, Wilford. N., "Report to the Utah State Fusion/Energy Council on the Analysis of Selected Pons Fleischmann Calorimetric Data," Second Annual Conference on Cold Fusion, Como, Italy: Societa Italiana di Fisica, Bologna, Italy, (1991)
3. Bard, Alan J., Barnes, Charlie, Birnbaum, Howard, "Comments on SRI RP-3170 Review Meeting 25-26 March 1991", Unpublished private report, (1991)
4. Miles, Melvin, et al., "Correlation of excess power and helium production during D2O and H2O electrolysis using palladium cathodes," Journal of Electroanalytical Chemistry, 1993. 346: (1993), p. 99   Also similarly published Fusion Technology, Vol. 25, (1994), p. 478.
5. Garwin, Richard L., Lewis, Nathan, "Report from SRI Visit October 19, 1993," Unpublished private report, (1993)
6. Melich, Michael E., Hansen, Wilford N., "Back to the Future, The Fleischmann-Pons Effect in 1994," Fourth International Conference on Cold Fusion, Lahaina, Maui: Electric Power Research Institute, (1993)
7. Dufour, Jacques, et al., J. Foos, J.P. Millot, Shell Research/ CNAM Laboratoire des Sciences Nucléaires 2 rue Conté 75 003 Paris, 9 April 1995, Excess energy in the system Palladium/Hydrogen isotopes, Measurements of the excess energy per atom hydrogen, Listed in index as ICCF5 paper # 604, but unpublished
8. Lautzenhiser*, T., Phelps*, D.W., Eisner**, M., (* Amoco, ** University of Houston,) Cold Fusion: Report on a Recent Amoco Experiment, Amoco Production Company, Report T-90-E-02, 90081ART0082, 19, March 1990, Private Report
9. Hansen, W.N., "Report to the Utah State Fusion/Energy Council on the Analysis of Selected Pons Fleischmann Calorimetric Data," Second Annual Conference on Cold Fusion, Como, Italy, Societa Italiana di Fisica, Bologna, Italy, (1991)

10. Hansen, W.N., and Melich, M.E., "Pd/D Calorimetry - The Key to the F/P Effect and a Challenge to Science in Fourth International Conference on Cold Fusion," Lahaina, Maui: Electric Power Research Institute 3412 Hillview Ave., Palo Alto, CA 94304, Transactions of Fusion Technology, Vol. 26, No. 4T, Part 2, (December 1994), p. 355

11. Melich, M.E. and Hansen, W.N., "Back to the Future, The Fleischmann-Pons Effect in 1994," Fourth International Conference on Cold Fusion, Lahaina, Maui: Electric Power Research Institute 3412 Hillview Ave., Palo Alto, CA 94304, (1994)

12. Lautzenhiser, T., Phelps, D.W., Eisner, M., "Cold Fusion: Report on a Recent Amoco Experiment," Amoco Production Co., Report T-90-E-02, 90081ART0082, March 19, 1990, Private Report, Note: Paper is listed in Abstracts of Fifth International Conference on Cold Fusion 9-13 April, 1995 - Monte Carlo, Monaco but full paper was never published in proceedings, (1995)

13. Dufour, J., Foos, J., Millot, J.P., "Excess Energy in the System Palladium/Hydrogen Isotopes, Measurements of the Excess Energy per Atom Hydrogen," Fifth International Conference on Cold Fusion 9-13 April, 1995 - Monte Carlo, Monaco, (1995)

14. Dufour, Jacques, private communications, (June 15, 2004)

15. Dufour, Jacques, private communications, (July 1, 2004)

16. Eisner. M, private communications, (Feb. 14, 2004)

Chapter 16, Cold Fusion: A Forbidden Topic

1. Letts, Dennis, private communications, (Sept. 19, 2003)
2. Oriani, Richard, private communications, (Aug. 6, 2004)
3. Lindley, David, "Letter to Oriani," (Sept. 20, 1989)
4. Oriani, Richard, et al., "Calorimetric Measurements of Excess Power Output During the Cathodic Charging of Deuterium into Palladium," Fusion Technology, Vol. 18, (1990), p. 652
5. Miles, Melvin, private communications, (Aug. 7, 2004)
6. Miles, Melvin, private communications, (Aug. 29, 2004)
7. Miles, Melvin, "Letter to Kohl", (Jan. 12, 2002)
8. Miles, Melvin, private communications, (July 12, 2004)
9. Miles, Melvin, private communications, (Aug. 7, 2004)
10. De Ninno, Antonella, private communications, (Oct. 10, 2003)
11. Bertsch, George, "Letter to Edmund Storms," (Aug 10, 2001)

Chapter 17, Silence and Neglect

1. Park, Robert, private communications, (Nov. 12, 2003)
2. Storms, Edmund, private communications, (Nov. 11, 2003)
3. Garwin, Richard (as quoted by Taubes, Gary), Bad Science: The Short Life and Weird Times of Cold Fusion, (New York, Random House, June 15, 1993), p. 319
4. Beaudette, Charles, Excess Heat & Why Cold Fusion Research Prevailed, 2nd ed., South Bristol, Maine, Oak Grove Press, (2002), p. 82
5. Garwin, Richard L., Lewis, Nathan, "Private Report to Dr. Lee M. Hammarstrom SAF/SS, 4C-1052 Pentagon, D.C. regarding SRI Visit Oct. 19, 1993," (Dec. 23, 1993)
6. Hansen, Lee, private communications, (Dec. 2, 2003)
7. Fleischmann, Martin, private communications, (July 15, 2004)
8. Bard, Alan J., Report to EPRI, "Private Report: Comments on SRI RP-3170 Review Meeting 25-26 March 1991," (May 13, 1992)
9. Bard, Allan, (as quoted by Feder, Tony) "DOE Warms to Cold Fusion" *Physics Today*, April 1, 2004)
10. McKubre, Michael, and Passell, Tom, private communications
11. McKubre, Michael, private communications, (Jan. 15, 2004)
12. Beaudette, Charles, *Excess Heat & Why Cold Fusion Research Prevailed*, 2nd ed., South Bristol, Maine, Oak Grove Press, (2002), p. 141

Chapter 18, Pathological Criticism

1. Begley, Sharon, "Cold Fusion Isn't Dead, It's Just Withering From Scientific Neglect," *Wall Street Journal*, (p. 5, 2003)
2. Fleischmann, Martin, (in video by Mallove, Eugene), "Cold Fusion: Fire from Water," (1996)
3. http://www.anomalist.com/milestones/truzzi.html
4. Beaty, William J., http://amasci.com/pathsk2.txt
5. Boerner, Rochus, http://www.suppressedscience.net/skepticism.html
6. McKubre, Michael, private communications, (Jan. 15, 2004)
7. Rothwell, Jed, private communications, (July 22, 2004)
8. Storms, Edmund, private communications, (Nov. 25, 2003)
9. Rothwell, Jed, private communications, (Oct 3, 2003)
10. Feshbach, Herman, (as quoted by Mallove, Eugene), "MIT Special Report,"Infinite Energy, 1999. 4(24), (1999)
11. Gratzer, Walter, *The Undergrowth of Science: Delusion, Self-Deception, and Human Frailty*, Oxford University Press, New York, N.Y. (2000)
12. Gratzer, Walter, private communications, (Nov. 10, 2003)

13. Gratzer, Walter, private communications, (Nov. 11, 2003)
14. Park, Robert, private communications, (Nov. 12, 2003)
15. Koonin, Steven, private communications, (Jan. 25, 2004)
16. Lewis, Nathan, private communications, (Jan. 26, 2004)
17. Happer, William, private communications, (Jan. 26, 2004)
18. Happer, William, (as quoted by Feder, Tony) "DOE Warms to Cold Fusion" *Physics Today*, April 1, 2004)
19. Close, Frank, *Too Hot to Handle: The Race for Cold Fusion, Princeton University Press*, Princeton, New Jersey, (1991)
20. Williams, David, private communications, (Jan. 24, 2004)
21. Close, Frank, private communications, (Dec. 16, 2003)
22. Close, Frank, private communications, (Dec. 17, 2003)

Chapter 19, 15 Years of Progress

1. Karabut, Alexander, private communications, (Nov. 12, 2003)
2. Srinivasan, Mahadeva, private communications, (Oct. 1, 2003)
3. Nagel, David, "ICCF-10 Public Talk, "http://www.newenergytimes.com, (Aug. 25, 2003)
4. Wood, Lowell, private communications, (Nov. 2, 2003)
5. Nagel, David, private communications, (Jan. 14, 2004)
6. Gordon, Frank E. from the forward to "A Decade of Research at Navy Laboratories Vol. 1," by Stan Szpak et al., San Diego, CA., SPAWAR Systems Center, (2002)
7. Nagel, David, private communications, (Jan. 31, 2004)
8. Mallove, Eugene, (as quoted by Kenneth Chang), "U.S. Will Give Cold Fusion Second Look, After 15 Years," *The New York Times,* (Mar. 25, 2004)

Chapter 20, Objections Overturned

1. Storms, Edmund, "Cold Fusion: An Objective Assessment," http://edstorms.com/review8.htm, (2001)
2. See refs. Chapter 23, 2-8

Chapter 21, Reproducibility

1. McKubre, Michael, "Too Close to the Sun," BBC Horizon, (March 21, 1994)

2. Scaramuzzi, Francesco, "Whatever Happened to Cold Fusion?" *Accountability in Research*, 2000. 8 (2002), p. 59
3. McKubre, Michael, private communications, (Aug. 11, 2004)
4. Storms, Edmund, private communications, (Feb. 17, 2004)
5. Storms, Edmund, "Cold Fusion: An Objective Assessment," http://edstorms.com/review8.html, (2001)
6. McKubre, Michael, private communications, (Sept. 1, 2004)
7. Nagel, David, "ICCF-10 Public Talk," http://www.newenergytimes.com, (Aug. 25, 2003)
8. Letts, Dennis, private communications, (Sept. 4, 2004)
9. Mallove, Eugene, "Breaking Through, an Editorial," *Infinite Energy Magazine*, No. 51, (Sept. 2003), and Letts, Dennis, private communications, (Jan. 15, 2004)
10. Nagel, David, "ICCF-10 Public Talk," http://www.newenergytimes.com, (Aug. 25, 2003)
11. De Ninno, Antonella, private communications, (Oct. 9, 2003)
12. Del Guidice, Emilio, private communications, (Sept. 22, 2003)
13. Storms, Edmund, "Cold Fusion Revisited," http://www.edstorms.com/review5.html
14. Storms, Edmund, "Cold Fusion: An Objective Assessment," http://edstorms.com/review8.html, (2001), also "A Student's Guide to Cold Fusion," http://www.lenr-canr.org/StudentsGuide.htm
15. Nagel, David, "ICCF-10 Public Talk," http://www.newenergytimes.com, (Aug. 25, 2003) and private communications, (Dec. 13, 2003)

Chapter 22, Nuclear Evidence: Tritium

1. Nagel, David, "ICCF-10 Public Talk," http://www.newenergytimes.com, (Aug. 25, 2003)
2. Srinivasan, Mahadeva, (in video by Mallove, Eugene), "Cold Fusion: Fire from Water," (1996)
3. Storms, Edmund, private communications, (Feb. 22 2003)
4. Storms, Edmund, and Talcott, Carol, "Electrolytic Tritium Production," *Fusion Technology*, Vol. 17, (1990) p. 680)
5. Storms, Edmund, private communications, (Feb. 22 2003)
6. Bockris, John, private communications, (July 10, 2004)
7. Santucci, Joseph, "Technology Update," Northern States Power Company, 1989)
8. Passell, Tom, private communications, (June 30, 2004)

9. Bockris, John, "Early Contributions from Workers at Texas A&M University to (So-Called) Low Energy Nuclear Reactions," *Journal of New Energy*, Vol. 4, No. 2 (1999) p. 40) also, Packham, N. J. C., Wolf, K. L., Wass, J. C. , Kainthla, R. C., Bockris, John O.M., "Production of Tritium from D2O Electrolysis at a Palladium Cathode," *Journal of Electroanalytical Chemistry*, V. 289, (1989), p. 451

10. Bockris, John, (in video by Mallove, Eugene), "Cold Fusion: Fire from Water," (1996)

11. Edmund Storms, private communications, (July 5, 2004)

12. Mallove, Eugene, Fire from Ice: Searching for the Truth Behind the Cold Fusion Furor, Infinite Energy Press, Bow, N.H., (1991), p. 241

13. Bockris, John, private communications, (July 10, 2004)

14. Bockris, John, July 9, 1990 "Answer to an Assault on Legitimate Research, & Suggestions of Fraud, in an Article Published in Science," (July 9, 1990)

15. Bockris, John, private communications, (July 10, 2004)

16. Bockris, John, "Note Concerning an Article by Taubes which was Published in Science", (June 15, 1990)

17. Bockris, John, July 9, 1990 "Answer to an Assault on Legitimate Research, & Suggestions of Fraud, in an Article Published in Science," (July 9, 1990)

18. Bockris, John, private communications, (July 10, 2004)

19. Packham, Nigel, private communications, (July 7, 2004)

20. Bockris, John, private communications, (July 10, 2004)

21. Bockris, John, "Accountability and Academic Freedom - The Battle Concerning Research on Cold Fusion at Texas A&M University," Accountability in Research, Vol. 8, (2000), p. 103

22. George, Russ, private communications, (July 22, 2004)

23. Bockris, John, private communications, (July 10, 2004)

24. Bockris, John, "Note Concerning an Article by Taubes which was Published in Science", (June 15, 1990)

25. Bockris, John, private communications, (July 10, 2004)

26. Bockris, John, July 9, 1990 "Answer to an Assault on Legitimate Research, & Suggestions of Fraud, in an Article Published in Science," (July 9, 1990)

27. Wolf, Kevin, (as reported by,) Bishop, Jerry, "Scientist Says `Cold Fusion' Tests May Have Had Some Impure Rods." Wall Street Journal, (Jun 7, 1990)

28. Will, Fritz, et. al., Fusion Technology, V.22 (1992), p.146)

29. Bockris, John, "Note Concerning an Article by Taubes which was Published in Science", (June 15, 1990)

30. Bockris, John, "Letter to the editor of Science," (June 29, 1990)

31. Bockris, John, July 9, 1990 "Answer to an Assault on Legitimate Research, & Suggestions of Fraud, in an Article Published in Science," (July 9, 1990)

32. Bockris, John, "Early Contributions from Workers at Texas A&M University to (So-Called) Low Energy Nuclear Reactions," Journal of New Energy, Vol. 4, No. 2 (2000) p. 40

33. Packham, Nigel, private communications, (July 7, 2004)
34. Bockris, John, "Accountability and Academic Freedom - The Battle Concerning Research on Cold Fusion at Texas A&M University," Accountability in Research, Vol. 8, (2000), p. 103
35. Bockris, John, July 9, 1990 "Answer to an Assault on Legitimate Research, & Suggestions of Fraud, in an Article Published in Science," (July 9, 1990)
36. Miley, George, (in video by Mallove, Eugene), "Cold Fusion: Fire from Water," (1996)
37. Epstein, Mike "Academic Freedom or Scientific Misconduct?" Journal of Scientific Exploration, Vol. 8/1 (1994), also Epstein, Mike, "Book Review of Bad Science: The Short Life and Weird Times of Cold Fusion," http://www.spectrometer.org/path/taubes.html)

Chapter 23, Helium-4, a Harmless Byproduct

1. Storms, Edmund, "Cold Fusion Revisited" http://home.netcom.com/~storms2/review5.html, (1998)
2. Storms, Edmund, private communications, (Nov. 4, 2003), and Storms, Edmund, "Cold Fusion: An Objective Assessment," http://edstorms.com/review8.html, (2001)
3. Miles, M., "Correlation of Excess Enthalpy and Helium-4 Production: A Review," Tenth International Conference on Cold Fusion, Cambridge, Mass., (2003)
4. Bush, Benjamin F., et al., "Helium Production during the Electrolysis of D2O in Cold Fusion Experiments," J. Electroanal. Chem., 304, (1991), p. 271
5. Bush, Benjamin, F., Lagowski, J. J., "Methods of Generating Excess Heat With the Pons and Fleischmann Effect: Rigorous and Cost-Effective Calorimetry, Nuclear Products Analysis of the Cathode and Helium Analysis," The Seventh International Conference on Cold Fusion, Vancouver, Canada: ENECO, Inc., Salt Lake City, Utah, (1998), p. 38
6. McKubre, M., et al., "The Emergence of a Coherent Explanation for Anomalies Observed in D/Pd and H/Pd System: Evidence for 4He and 3He Production," 8th International Conference on Cold Fusion. Lerici (La Spezia), Italy: Italian Physical Society, Bologna, Italy, (2000)
7. De Ninno, Antonella, et al., "Experimental Evidence of 4He Production in a Cold Fusion Experiment," ENEA - Unita Tecnico Scientfica Fusione Centro Ricerche Frascati, Roma, (2002)
8. Gozzi, D., et al., "X-ray, Heat Excess and 4He in the D:Pd System," Journal of Electroanalytical Chemistry 452, (1998)
9. Rothwell, Jed, "Introduction to the Cold Fusion Experiments of Melvin Miles," www.lenr-canr.org

10. Rothwell, Jed, "Introduction to the Cold Fusion Experiments of Melvin Miles," www.lenr-canr.org, also, Miles, Melvin, "Correlation of Excess Enthalpy and Helium-4 Production: A Review," Proceedings of the 10th International Conference on Cold Fusion, Cambridge, Mass. (2003)
11. McKubre, M., et al., "The Emergence of a Coherent Explanation for Anomalies Observed in D/Pd and H/Pd System: Evidence for 4He and 3He Production," 8th International Conference on Cold Fusion. Lerici (La Spezia), Italy: Italian Physical Society, Bologna, Italy, (2000)
12. Ibid.
13. Del Guidice, Emilio, private communications, (Sept. 22, 2003)
14. Nagel, David, "ICCF-10 Public Talk", (Aug. 25, 2003)

Chapter 24, Neutrons Found

1. Jones, Steven, E. et al., "Charged-particle Emissions from Metal Deuterides," Tenth International Conference on Cold Fusion, Cambridge, Mass., (2003)
2. Storms, Edmund, 57 neutrons/hr = 10-1 (0.0158) fusion reactions per second. Fleischmann-Pons-type cold fusion experiment, yielding one watt of excess heat, will require 2.6x1011 fusion reactions per second. eV = 1.60E-12 erg/event, 24 MeV= 3.84E-05 erg/event, =3.84E-12 J/event, =3.84E-12 watt-sec/event, =2.60E+11 events/watt-sec.
3. Huizenga, John R., "Cold Fusion, The Scientific Fiasco of the Century," New York, Oxford University Press, (1993) p. 214
4. Nagel, David, "ICCF-10 Public Talk", (Aug. 25, 2003)

Chapter 25, The Race for a Nobel Prize-Winning Theory

1. Beaudette, Charles, "Excess Heat & Why Cold Fusion Research Prevailed, 2nd ed.", South Bristol, Maine, Oak Grove Press, (2002), p. 87
2. Mckubre, Michael, (in video by Mallove, Eugene), "Cold Fusion: Fire from Water," (1996)
3. Nagel, David, "ICCF-10 Public Talk", (Aug. 25, 2003), and private communications, (Dec. 13, 2003)
4. Storms, Edmund, private communications, (Feb. 16, 2003)
5. Hagelstein, Peter, private communications, (Jan. 9, 2004)
6. McKubre, Michael, private communications, (Jan. 15, 2004)
7. Li, Xing Zhong, et al., "Sub-Barrier Fusion and Selective Resonant Tunneling," *Physical Review C*, V. 61, 024610 (Jan. 19, 2000)
8. Roth, J. Reece, private communications, (Nov. 8, 2003)

9. Li, X.Z., "Nuclear Physics for Nuclear Fusion," *Fusion Science and Technology*, Vol. 41, p. 63, (2002)
10. Li, Xing Zhong, private communications, (June 16, 2004)
11. Li, X.Z., "Nuclear Physics for Nuclear Fusion," *Fusion Science and Technology*, Vol. 41, p. 63, (2002)

Chapter 26, Nuclear Energy from Normal Water

1. Chubb, Scott, private communications, (Feb. 25, 2004)
2. Biberian, Jean-Paul, (in video by Mallove, Eugene), "Cold Fusion: Fire from Water," (1996)
3. Biberian, Jean-Paul, private communications, (July 30, 2004)
4. Storms, Edmund, (in video by Mallove, Eugene), "Cold Fusion: Fire from Water," (1996)
5. Miley, George M., "Progress in Thin Film LENR Research," The Ninth International Conference on Cold Fusion. Beijing, China: Tsinghua University, (2002)
6. Corey, James, "Energetic Materials: History of and Current Claims for Low Energy Nuclear Reactions," 2003 Energetic Materials Intelligence Symposium, (Sept. 10-12, 2003), and Miley, George, private communications, (Feb. 18, 2004)

Chapter 27, Nuclear Transmutations through Chemistry

1. Miley, G.H., Shrestha, P., "Review of Transmutation Reactions in Solids," Tenth International Conference on Cold Fusion, Cambridge, Mass, (2003)
2. Iwamura, Yasuhiro, et al., "Detection of Anomalous Elements, X-Ray and Excess Heat Induced by Continuous Diffusion of Deuterium Through Multi-Layer Cathode (Pd/Cao/Pd)" presented at the Seventh International Conference on Cold Fusion in Vancouver, Canada, (1998)
3. Iwamura, Yasuhiro, et al., "Elemental Analysis of Pd Complexes: Effects of D2 Gas Permeation," *Japanese Journal of Applied Physics*, Vol. 41, (2002) p. 4642
4. Iwamura, Yasuhiro, private communications, (July 2, 2004)
5. Takahashi, Akito, private communications, Sep. 18, 2003)

Chapter 28, Technical Summary of Cold Fusion (August 2003)

(none)

Chapter 29, Threats to Academic Freedom

1. Anderson, Philip W., "Why Do They Leave Physics?," *Physics Today*, (Sept. 1999)
2. McKubre, Michael, private communications, (Aug. 22, 2003)
3. Miles, Melvin, private communications, (Sept. 14, 2003)
4. Bockris, John, private communications, (July 10, 2004)
5. Bockris, John, "Accountability and Academic Freedom - The Battle Concerning Research on Cold Fusion at Texas A&M University," Accountability in Research, Vol. 8, (2000), p. 103
6. Mallove, Eugene, "Letter to Duane Kraemer," (Jan. 17, 1994)
7. Hagelstein, Peter, "Letter to John Bockris," (Dec. 15, 1993)
8. Bockris, Lillian, "Letter to Robert Kennedy," (Jan. 3, 1994)
9. Bockris, John, "Accountability and Academic Freedom - The Battle Concerning Research on Cold Fusion at Texas A&M University," Accountability in Research, Vol. 8, (2000), p. 103
10. Epstein, Mike, "Academic Freedom or Scientific Misconduct?", Journal of Scientific Exploration, Vol. 8/1, (1994)

Chapter 30, National Security

1. Gerischer, Heinz, (as quoted by Dec. 30, 1993 letter from Eagleton, Robert to Dean Gage, also as quoted by Jan. 17, 1994 letter from Robert Bass to Duane Kraemer
2. Recent Developments in Fusion Energy Research," 101st Cong., 1st Sess., No. 46, (April 26, 1989)
3. Anonymous, private communications (June 14, 2004)
4. Anonymous, private communications, (Aug. 1, 2004)

Chapter 31, Lessons Learned

1. Gaud, William "The Scientific Process,"
   http://jan.ucc.nau.edu/~gaud/bio372/class/behavior/sciproc.htm
2. Cotton, John, http://www.physics.smu.edu/~jcotton/ph3333/class09.htm, http://www.physics.smu.edu/~jcotton/ph3333/
3. Beaudette, Charles, *Excess Heat & Why Cold Fusion Research Prevailed, 2nd ed.*, South Bristol, Maine, Oak Grove Press, (2002), p. 339,343
4. Maddox, John, "Too Close to the Sun" (BBC Horizon/CBC) (March 21, 1994)

Chapter 32, Speculation about the Future

1. Nagel, David, private communications, (July 30, 2004)
2. Fleischmann, M., S. Pons, and M. Hawkins, "Electrochemically induced nuclear fusion of deuterium," *Journal of Electroanalytical Chemistry*, Vol. 261, p. 301 and errata in Vol. 263 (1989)
3. Fleischmann, M. and S. Pons, "Calorimetry of the Pd-D_2O system: from simplicity via complications to simplicity," Physics Letters A, Vol. 176, (1993), p. 118
4. Preparata, Giuliano, et al., "Isoperibolic calorimetry on modified Fleischmann-Pons cells," *Journal of Electroanalytical Chemistry*, 411, 9 (1996)
5. Fleischmann, Martin, private communications, (July 30, 2004)
6. De Ninno, Antonella, private communications, (Aug. 2, 2004)
7. Storms, Edmund, private communications, (Aug. 4, 2004)
8. Clarke, Arthur C., (in video by Mallove, Eugene), "Cold Fusion: Fire from Water," (1996)
9. Miles, Melvin H., et al., "Anomalous Effects in Deuterated Systems, Final Report," NAWCWPNS Technical Publication 8302, Research and Technology Division, Naval Air Warfare Center Weapons Division China Lake, (Sept. 1996)
10. Nagel, David, ICCF-10 Public Talk," (Aug. 25, 2003)
11. Storms, Edmund, http://home.netcom.com/~storms2/table2cf.html, and Beaudette, Charles, *Excess Heat & Why Cold Fusion Research Prevailed, 2nd ed.*, South Bristol, Maine, Oak Grove Press, (2002), p. 366
12. Nagel, David J., "Fusion Physics and Philosophy," *Accountability in Research*, 8, (2000), p.137
13. Estimates based on miscellaneous reports of DARPA and Navy funding.
14. Mizuno, Tadahiko," Nuclear Transmutation: The Reality of Cold Fusion," Infinite Energy Press, Bow, New Hampshire, (1998); Fleischmann, Martin, and Pons, Stanley, "Calorimetry of the Pd-D_2O system: from simplicity via complications to simplicity," *Physics Letters A*, V. 176 (1993), p. 118; Miles, Melvin, et al., "Thermal Behavior of Polarized Pd/D Electrodes Prepared by Co-Deposition," The Ninth International Conference on Cold Fusion, Beijing, China, (2002); Szpak, Stan, et al., "Thermal Behavior of Polarized Pd/D Electrodes Prepared by Co-deposition," *Thermochimica Acta*, Vol. 410, p. 101, (2004)
15. Arata, Yoshiaki, Zhang, Yue-Chang, "Anomalous production of gaseous 4He at the inside of 'DS cathode' during D_2O-electrolysis," *Proc. Jpn. Acad.*, Ser. B, 75: p. 281 (1999); Arata, Yoshiaki, Zhang, Yue-Chang, "A new energy caused by 'Spillover-deuterium,'" *Proc. Jpn. Acad.*, Ser. B, 70 ser. B: p. 106, (1994)
16. Storms, Edmund, "A Critical Review of the "Cold Fusion" Effect", *Journal of Scientific Exploration,* 10, #2, p. 185, (1996)
17. Scaramuzzi, Francesco, "Whatever Happened to Cold Fusion?"

Accountability in Research, 2000. 8 (2002), p. 59

18. Biberian, Jean Paul, (in video by Mallove, Eugene), "Cold Fusion: Fire from Water," (1996)

19. Clarke, Sir Arthur C., (in video by Mallove, Eugene), "Cold Fusion: Fire from Water," (1996)\

20. Bockris, John, (in video by Mallove, Eugene), "Cold Fusion: Fire from Water," (1996)

21. Roth, J. Reece, private communications, (Nov. 8, 2003)

22. Miley, George, (in video by Mallove, Eugene), "Cold Fusion: Fire from Water," (1996)

23. Storms, Edmund, private communications, (Feb. 22, 2002)

24. Sinha, Krityunjai Prasad, private communications, (Aug. 25, 2003)

25. Hubler, Dorothy, private communications, (June 28, 2004)

26. Fleischmann, Martin, "Too Close to the Sun," BBC Horizon, (March 21, 1994)

Bibliography

Anderson, Philip W., "Why Do They Leave Physics?," *Physics Today*, (Sept. 1999)

Arata, Yoshiaki, Zhang, Yue-Chang, "Anomalous production of gaseous 4He at the inside of 'DS cathode' during D_2O-electrolysis," *Proc. Jpn. Acad.*, Ser. B, 75: p. 281 (1999)

Arata, Yoshiaki, Zhang, Yue-Chang, "A new energy caused by 'Spillover-deuterium,'" *Proc. Jpn. Acad.*, Ser. B, 70 ser. B: p. 106, (1994)

Bard, Alan J., Report to EPRI, "*Private Report: Comments on SRI RP-3170 Review Meeting 25-26 March 1991,*" (May 13, 1992)

Beaudette, Charles, *Excess Heat & Why Cold Fusion Research Prevailed, 2nd ed.*, South Bristol, Maine, Oak Grove Press, (2002), p.87

Begley, Sharon, "Cold Fusion Isn't Dead, It's Just Withering From Scientific Neglect," *The Wall Street Journal,* (Sept. 5, 2003)

Bockris, John, "Accountability and Academic Freedom - The Battle Concerning Research on Cold Fusion at Texas A&M University," Accountability in Research, Vol. 8, (2000), p. 103

Bockris, John, "Early Contributions from Workers at Texas A&M University to (So-Called) Low Energy Nuclear Reactions," Journal of New Energy, Vol. 4, No. 2 (1999) p. 40)

Bush, Benjamin F., et al., "Helium Production during the Electrolysis of D2O in Cold Fusion Experiments," *J. Electroanal. Chem., 304,* (1991), p. 271

Bush, Benjamin, F., Lagowski, J. J., "Methods of Generating Excess Heat With the Pons and Fleischmann Effect: Rigorous and Cost-Effective Calorimetry, Nuclear Products Analysis of the Cathode and Helium Analysis," *The Seventh International Conference on Cold Fusion, Vancouver, Canada: ENECO, Inc., Salt Lake City, Utah,* (1998), p. 38

Bush, Robert, (in video by Mallove, Eugene), "Cold Fusion: Fire from Water," (1996)

Corey, James, "Energetic Materials: History of and Current Claims for Low Energy Nuclear Reactions," *2003 Energetic Materials Intelligence Symposium,* (Sept. 10-12, 2003)

De Ninno, Antonella, et al., "Experimental Evidence of 4He Production in a Cold Fusion Experiment," *ENEA - Unita Tecnico Scientfica Fusione Centro Ricerche Frascati,* (2002)

Dufour, J., Foos, J., Millot, J.P., "Excess Energy in the System Palladium/Hydrogen Isotopes, Measurements of the Excess Energy per Atom Hydrogen," *Fifth International Conference on Cold Fusion 9-13 April, 1995 - Monte Carlo, Monaco,* (1995)

286

Epstein, Mike, "Academic Freedom or Scientific Misconduct?", Journal of Scientific Exploration, Vol. 8/1, (1994)

Feshbach, Herman, (as quoted by Mallove, Eugene), "MIT Special Report,"*Infinite Energy, 1999. 4(24),* (1999)

Fleischmann, M., S. Pons, and M. Hawkins, *Electrochemically induced nuclear fusion of deuterium. J. Electroanal. Chem., 261, p. 301 and errata in Vol. 263, (1989)*

Fleischmann, M. and S. Pons, "Calorimetry of the Pd-D_2O system: from simplicity via complications to simplicity," Physics Letters A, Vol. 176, (1993), p. 118

Garwin, Richard L., Lewis, Nathan, "*Private Report to Dr. Lee M. Hammarstrom SAF/SS, 4C-1052 Pentagon, D.C. regarding SRI Visit Oct. 19, 1993,*" (Dec. 23, 1993)

Gaud, William "The Scientific Process," http://jan.ucc/nau.edu/~gaud/bio372/class/behavior/sciproc.htm

Goodstein, David, "Whatever Happened to Cold Fusion?" *Accountability in Research, 2000. 8* (2002), p. 59

Gordon, Frank E. from the forward to "A Decade of Research at Navy Laboratories Vol. 1," by Stan Szpak et al., *San Diego, CA., SPAWAR Systems Center*, (2002)

Gozzi, D., et al., "X-ray, Heat Excess and 4He in the D:Pd System," *Journal of Electroanalytical Chemistry 452,* (1998)

Hansen, W.N. and Melich, M.E., "Pd/D Calorimetry - The Key to the F/P Effect and a Challenge to Science," *Fourth International Conference on Cold Fusion, Lahaina, Maui: Electric Power Research Institute 3412 Hillview Ave., Palo Alto, CA 94304,* (1993), and *Transactions of Fusion Technology, Vol. 26, Number 4T, Part 2,* (December 1994), p. 355

Hansen, W.N., "Report to the Utah State Fusion/Energy Council on the Analysis of Selected Pons Fleischmann Calorimetric Data," *Second Annual Conference on Cold Fusion, Como, Italy,* Societa Italiana di Fisica, Bologna, Italy, (1991)

Happer, William (as quoted by Taubes, Gary), *Bad Science: The Short Life and Weird Times of Cold Fusion,* (New York, Random House, June 15, 1993), p. 305

Huizenga, John R., *Cold Fusion, The Scientific Fiasco of the Century,* New York, Oxford University Press, (1993), p. 297

Iwamura, Yasuhiro, et al., "Detection of Anomalous Elements, X-Ray and Excess Heat Induced by Continuous Diffusion of Deuterium Through Multi-Layer Cathode (Pd/Cao/Pd)" presented at the Seventh International Conference on Cold Fusion in Vancouver, Canada, (1998)

Iwamura, Yasuhiro, et al., "Elemental Analysis of Pd Complexes: Effects of D2 Gas Permeation," Japanese Journal of Applied Physics, Vol. 41, (2002) p. 4642,

Koonin, Steven, (as quoted by Charles Beaudette), *Excess Heat & Why Cold Fusion Research Prevailed, 2nd ed.,* South Bristol, Maine, Oak Grove Press, (2002), p. 79

287

Lautzenhiser, T., Phelps, D.W., Eisner, M., "Cold Fusion: Report on a Recent Amoco Experiment," *Amoco Production Co., Report T-90-E-02, 90081ART0082, March 19, 1990, Private Report, Note: Paper is listed in Abstracts of Fifth International Conference on Cold Fusion 9-13 April, 1995 - Monte Carlo, Monaco but full paper was never published in proceedings,* (1995)

Lewis, Nathan, (in video by Mallove, Eugene), "Cold Fusion: Fire from Water," (1996)

Li, Xing Zhong, et al., "Sub-Barrier Fusion and Selective Resonant Tunneling," Physical Review C, V. 61, 024610 (Jan. 19, 2000)

Li, Xing Zhong, et al., "Nuclear Physics for Nuclear Fusion," Fusion Science and Technology, Vol. 41, p. 63 (2002)

Lipson, Andrei, G., et al., "Observation of neutrons accompanying cavitation in deuterium containing media,"Soviet Technical Physics Letters, 16(10), (1990), p. 763. Translated by AIP # 0360-120X/90/10 0763-02, Lipson, Andri, G., et al., "Generation of nuclear fusion products by combined action of cavitation and electrolysis of titanium surface in deuterated electrolyte," Technical Physics Letters, 38(7), (1993), p. 623

Mallove, Eugene, "Breaking Through, an Editorial," *Infinite Energy, No. 51,* (Sept. 2003)

Mallove, Eugene, "MIT Special Report," *Infinite Energy, 1999 4(24),* (1999), p. 64, also at www.infinite-energy.com

Mallove, Eugene, Fire from Ice: Searching for the Truth Behind the Cold Fusion Furor, Infinite Energy Press, Bow, New Hampshire

McKubre, M., et al., "The Emergence of a Coherent Explanation for Anomalies Observed in D/Pd and H/Pd System: Evidence for 4He and 3He Production," *8th International Conference on Cold Fusion. Lerici (La Spezia), Italy: Italian Physical Society, Bologna, Italy,* (2000)

McKubre, Michael, "RADIO WEST," (by Douglas Fubbrezio), *KUER/PBS, a service of the University of Utah KUER,* (Nov. 27, 2002)

Melich, M.E., and Hansen, W.N., "Back to the Future, The Fleischmann-Pons Effect in 1994," *Fourth International Conference on Cold Fusion, Lahaina, Maui: Electric Power Research Institute 3412 Hillview Ave., Palo Alto, CA 94304,* (1993)

Melich, Michael, "Reasonable Doubt," (as quoted by Bennett Daviss), *New Scientist, Vol. 177 issue 2388,* (March 29, 2003), p. 36

Miles, Melvin H. and Bush, Benjamin F., "Calorimetric Principles and Problems in Pd-D2O Electrolysis", *The Third International Conference on Cold Fusion, Nagoya, Japan, Universal Academy Press Inc., Tokyo,* (1991), p. 113

Miles, M., et al., "Correlation of Excess Power and Helium Production during D2O and H2O Electrolysis Using Palladium Cathodes," *J. Electroanal. Chem., 346:* (1993), p. 99, also published, *Fusion Technol.,* Vol. 25, (1994), p. 478

Miles, M., "Correlation of Excess Enthalpy and Helium-4 Production: A Review," *Tenth International Conference on Cold Fusion, Cambridge, Mass.,* (2003)

288

Miles, Melvin H., et al., "Anomalous Effects in Deuterated Systems, Final Report," *NAWCWPNS Technical Publication 8302, Research and Technology Division, Naval Air Warfare Center Weapons Division China Lake,* (Sept. 1996)

Miles, M., et al., "Calorimetric Principles and Problems in Measurements of Excess Power During Pd-D2O Electrolysis," *J. Phys. Chem., Vol. 98,* (1994), p. 1948

Miles, Melvin, et al.,
"Thermal Behavior of Polarized Pd/D Electrodes Prepared by Co-Deposition," The Ninth International Conference on Cold Fusion, Beijing, China, (2002)

Miley, G.H., Shrestha, P., "Review of Transmutation Reactions in Solids," *Tenth International Conference on Cold Fusion, Cambridge, Mass.,* (2003)

Miley, George M., "Progress in Thin Film LENR Research," *The Ninth International Conference on Cold Fusion. Beijing, China: Tsinghua University,* (2002)

Mizuno, Tadahiko," Nuclear Transmutation: The Reality of Cold Fusion," Infinite Energy Press, Bow, New Hampshire, (1998)

Nagel, David, "ICCF-10 Public Talk," http://www.newenergytimes.com, (Aug. 25, 2003)

Nelson, Steve, http://www.madsci.org/posts/archives/Apr2003/1051645602.Ph.r.html

Noninski, V.C. and Noninski, C.I., "Notes on Two Papers Claiming No Evidence for the Existence of Excess Energy During the Electrolysis of 0.1 M LiOD/D2O with Palladium Cathodes," *Fusion Technology, Vol. 23,* (July 1993), p. 474-76

Oriani, Richard, A. et al., "Calorimetric Measurements of Excess Power Output During the Cathodic Charging of Deuterium into Palladium," Fusion Technology, 1990. 18: (1990) p. 652.

Preparata, Giuliano, et al., "Isoperibolic calorimetry on modified Fleischmann-Pons cells," *Journal of Electroanalytical Chemistry,* 411, 9 (1996)

Packham, N. J. C., Wolf, K. L., Wass, J. C. , Kainthla, R. C., Bockris, J. O.M., "Production of Tritium from D2O Electrolysis at a Palladium Cathode," Journal of Electroanalytical Chemistry, V. 289, (1989), p. 451)

Ramsey, Norman, in the preamble to "Report of the Energy Research Advisory Board to the United States Department of Energy," http://www.ncas.org/erab (November 1989)

Scaramuzzi, Francesco, "Whatever Happened to Cold Fusion?" Accountability in Research, 2000. 8 (2002), p. 59

Swartz, Mitchell, "Some Lessons From Optical Examination of the PFC Phase-II Calorimetric Curves," *Vol. 2, Proceedings: Fourth International Conference on Cold Fusion, sponsored by EPRI and the Office of Naval Research,* (1993)

Storms, Edmund, "Cold Fusion: An Objective Assessment," *http://edstorms.com/review8.htm,* (2001)

Storms, Edmund, "Cold Fusion Revisited," http://www.edstorms.com/review5.html

Storms, Edmund, "A Student's Guide to Cold Fusion," *http://www.lenr-canr.org/StudentsGuide.htm*

Storms, Edmund, "A Critical Review of the "Cold Fusion" Effect", *Journal of Scientific Exploration,* 10, #2, p. 185, (1996)

Szpak, Stan, et al., "Thermal Behavior of Polarized Pd/D Electrodes Prepared by Co-deposition," *Thermochimica Acta,* Vol. 410, p. 101, (2004)
Will, Fritz, et. al., Fusion Technology, V.22 (1992), p.146)

Index

cavitation fusion, see sonofusion and bubble fusion

Center for New Hydrogen Energy, 126

Champion, Joe, 231

chemical energy, 26-27, 37, 135, 261

chemically assisted nuclear reactions (canr), 11, 18

chemistry, not, 118-119, 207

China, 22, 58, 64, 240-241

China Lake, see Naval Air Warfare Center Weapons Division at China Lake,

Chubb, Scott, xii, 51, 210

Chubb, Talbot, 18, 131, 210

CIA, 182

Clarke, Arthur C., xv-xvii, 254, 260

Claytor, Thomas, 176

climate change, xvii, 19, 26

Close, Frank, 115, 146, 150, 196-197, 248

coal, used for electricity generation, 26-27, 32, 44-45, 254

Cöhn, Alfred, 70

cold fusion
  basic definition, 3
  basic experiment, 5
  branches, 222
  corroboration, 118, 124, 197
  commercial applications, 249, 254
  commercialization, earliest
estimated, 258

condensed matter nuclear science, (cmns), 11, 18

congress, U.S., 13, 38, 47, 73, 79, 92, 240

contamination, of heavy water, 167

contamination, of tritium, 178, 185

Corey, James, 57-58, 220

Cotton, Frank Albert, 232-233, 237

Cotton, John, 247

cover-up, 103, 248

Cravens, Dennis, 168, 169

critic, definition, 142

cross section (nuclear), 212

Curie, Pierre, 209, 259

curves, shifted, 106-108

cynic, definition, 142

D_2, 4

D_2O, 4

Daviss, Bennett, 155

De Ninno, Antonella, 129, 169, 195, 252, 253

debunking, 95-101, 103

Deffeyes, Kenneth S., 20

Del Guidice, Emilio, 169, 200, 252

Department of Defense, U.S., 154, 243

Department of Energy, 22, 34, 39-40, 71, 91
  2004 cold fusion review, xii, 18, 149, 154-157
  1989 cold fusion review, panel, 91-92, 205

depletion, see oil, peak oil

desalination, 255

deuterium, xv, 3-4, 11

DoE, see Department of Energy

Dufour, Jacques, 120-121

294

About the Authors

Steven B. Krivit has been conducting investigative research into cold fusion and other New Energy topics since 2000. The founder of New Energy Times, he has earned the respect of the worldwide cold fusion community. Krivit has become a media consultant on the subject. He earned a bachelor's degree in business management from National University in San Diego, California, and studied industrial design at the University of Bridgeport in Connecticut.

Nadine Winocur, Psy.D. is the editor for New Energy Times. In addition to her interests in New Energy, Winocur maintains a private psychotherapy practice and facilitates continuing education training in the field. Winocur earned her doctoral degree in psychology from Pepperdine University in Malibu, California.

Krivit and Winocur are married and live in Los Angeles with their two cats.

Steven B. Krivit and Nadine Winocur, Psy.D.
Authors of *The Rebirth of Cold Fusion*
(Photo by Steven Krivit)

About New Energy Times

New Energy Times is a company which brings to the general public original reporting on research in the field of leading-edge energy and power technologies. Its mission is to provide a forum which offers news and information about potential changes in energy technology. New Energy Times, whose current project is researching cold fusion, collects its data directly from researchers and from original scientific papers.

The New Energy Times staff has no affiliations with any organization, entity or party which invests in new-energy technologies.

Visit New Energy Times on the Web at: www.newenergytimes.com.